ERIC SCHAEFFER

Industry X.0

ERIC SCHAEFFER

Industry X.0

Realizing Digital Value in Industrial Sectors

Bibliographic information from the Deutsche Nationalbibliothek
The Deutsche Nationalbibliothek registers this publication in the Deutsche National-bibliografie. Detailed bibliographic information can be retrieved at http://dnb.d-nb.de
British Library Cataloguing-in-Publication Data
A CIP record for this book is available from the British Library.
Library of Congress Cataloging-in-Publication Data
A CIP record for this book is available from the Library of Congress.

Published in Germany in 2017 by Redline Verlag, an imprint of Münchner Verlagsgruppe GmbH, Munich, Germany, as "Industry X.0. Realizing Digital Value in Industrial Sectors" by Eric Schaeffer.
Nymphenburger Str. 86
D-80636 München, Germany
www.redline-verlag.de

ISBN Print 978-3-86881-654-9

Edition Kogan Page 2017
Published and distributed in Great Britain, United States and India by Kogan Page Limited.
ISBN 978-0749481469
ISBN ebook: 978-0749481490

2nd Floor, 45 Gee Street
London EC1V 3RS
United Kingdom
www.koganpage.com

MPHC Marketing
c/o Martin P Hill Consulting
122 W 27th St, 10th Floor
New York, NY 10001
USA

4737/23 Ansari Road
Daryaganj
New Delhi 110002
India

Coverdesign by Blomqvist Design
Photo: © Accenture
Typeset by Helmut Schaffer, Hofheim a. Ts.
Printed by GGP Media GmbH, Pößneck
Printed in Germany

Table of Contents

Chapter 7

Chapter 8

Preface

The world has become digitally connected to the point of no return. Each day around five million devices become linked up with either each other, the Internet or both. There are around 6.4bn data-communicating objects in the world and by 2020 this number is forecast to explode to around 20bn.[1] Our digital universe is in healthy expansion mode.

From this perspective, today's device boom – the wristband pulse monitors, smart watches, satnavs and intelligent thermostats – are just the overture to a long and eventful journey towards lives digitally augmented, supported and enabled in ways unlike anything humans have ever experienced before.

The advance is propelled by our craving for technical innovation and our tendency to adapt promptly to new ways of interacting and engaging with machines and devices as soon as they exist. We as consumers will keep asking why this or that gap in the market has not yet been filled by some device or software solution. Businesses – the focus of this book, hence the title "Industry X.0" – and their increasingly digitally native workforce, used to a highly digitized private lifestyle, will put the same kinds of questions to their industrial vendors, displaying a new form of "industrial consumerism."

At the core of this seismic upheaval sit Living Products, physical products reinvented as software-intelligent devices that act, think, and are closely and constantly aligned with their users and ecosystems.

Clearly, then, the industrial sphere, the sphere of technologically produced physical objects, will play a major part in the seminal trip towards the planet's digitization. Digital technologies will create a stage on which we as public, businesses and industry experts will pull off spectacular things in the coming years.

Consider the following: the first pharmacy staffed only by robots, is expected to open its doors in 2021;[2] sensorized medical pills that report back to the makers when patients have swallowed them are currently in development; Siemens is already successfully running prototypes of completely unmanned, self-organizing and hyper-productive industrial plants;[3] and raw materials giant Rio Tinto has huge mining operations based on automated trucks and drill systems provided by heavy equipment makers Caterpillar and Komatsu.[4] Cars, industrial machinery and tooling, pumps, circuit breakers – they can all be rendered Living Products by adding software intelligence.

The ship has clearly sailed for digital sceptics, both as citizens and business leaders. The industrial enterprise world, comprising two thirds of the world's gross domestic product, will be changed beyond recognition by digital technology, disrupting decades-old business habits, conventions and operating models. The ways in which labor works, machine-based processes are organized and information is shared will be turned on their heads. Strategic corporate thinking will be forced to incorporate completely new data-driven business models to secure a future for any enterprise. No wonder the US, Germany, China and Japan – all strongholds of successful industrial enterprises – have, with varying focus, put industrial digital transformation high on the agenda.

There is no turning back. What matters now is to make the most of the digital transformation. We have the opportunity to shape it. There is not one standard way to make it happen, the journey must be tailored to each enterprise individually.

That is why this book, unlike other publications, not only addresses the "why" of the industrial sphere's wholesale digitization but also, primarily, the "how," examining in detail the steps industrial businesses need to take to get the greatest positive effect and value from digital.

Packed with easily accessible actionable insights and suggestions, it should be a vital resource for industrial business leaders at all levels, C-suite and below as well as across all functions. It should help them discover, think through, adopt and implement the road-map necessary for their enterprises to head out for the new territory, and act as an *aide-memoire* as the journey progresses.

Acknowledgments

In this book I have managed to gather and shape forward-looking advice around a complex subject: the emergence of the Industrial Internet of Things (IIoT) and its transformation of the industrial sectors. I visited and revisited the topic in detail and assessed its ramifications for the enterprises affected. And I developed a good deal of thought leadership in the process.

All this would have been impossible without the input of a large number of knowledgeable people from beyond our core book team. I was fortunate to be able to tap a wide intellectual catchment area: corporate thinkers, co-consultants, and clients, based in the US, UK, Germany, France, Italy, Korea, Europe, Japan, and China, contributing either broad ideas that helped shape the general themes and scope of the book or practical industry experience, focused sector insights, and firm opinion to test our own thinking. Their input has been invaluable in shaping the book's observations, analyses and hypotheses.

To all of them I would like to express a sincere "Thank you." The support of every one of you individually was a *conditio sine qua non* for pulling this off and collectively represents a piece of vanguard consultancy thinking on what is currently one of the most pressing subjects in the business world.

At Accenture I wish to thank David Abood, Fabian Bohn, Christophe Brasselet, Jean Cabanes, Brian Doyle, Dan Elron, Andreas

Gissler, AJ Gupta, Francis Hintermann, Richard Holman, Venkatesh Iyer, Lisa-Cheng Jackson, Jitendra A. Kavathekar, Shinichiro Kohno, Bodo Körber, Guiseppe La Commare, JC Ledoux, Sebastien Lepicard, Mahesh Mahajan, Sarat Maitin, Brian May, Bruno le Moal, Eric Mokrenski, Massimo Pagella, Mark H. Pearson, Bruno Pfeiffer, Philippe Pruvost, Kevin Prendeville, Kausar Qazilbash, Wu Qi, Aidan Quilligan, Ganesan Ramachandran, Shugo Sohma, Ben Salama, Marcello Tamietti, Maxence Tilliette, Cedric Vatier, Patrick Vollmer, Ben Wang, and Will Zhang.

Special thanks must go to Sander van 't Noordende, Omar Abbosh, and Frank Riemensperger for their support, inspiration and thought leadership around the transformation of industries.

Within Accenture thanks are also owed to Georg Berger, Gemma Catchpole, Andreas Egetenmeyer, Sonja Fink, Ulf Henning, Fiona Morris and Matthias Wahrendorff, the closer team steering the publication, as well as to Jens Schadendorf, Titus Kroder, and John Moseley, who brought valuable experience and exceptional knowledge with regard to the writing and publishing of a book.

A big thank you also goes to Helen Kogan and Jenny Volich from Kogan Page, and Michael Wurster from Redline, as the publishers of this book, for their enduring commitment to and trust in this project.

Finally, and above all, I thank my wife Pascale for her patience, relentless support and love and my children William, Meryl and Edouard for the many and passionate discussions on the new digital economy. May this book help them navigate successfully through the change.

Introduction

Coinciding with the wholesale digital interlinking of society, the digital disruption and transformation of the industrial sphere is one of the world's current megatrends, affecting companies representing two thirds of global GDP.[1] Makers of cars, planes, trains, domestic appliances, heavy equipment and engineering technology, pharmaceuticals, and utility and raw materials businesses are all undergoing waves of technological upheaval as we speak.

Smartened, tightly connected, data-driven industrial products and processes are going to go mainstream in all advanced and many emerging countries very soon. Embedded in the wider trend towards the Internet of Things (IoT), its sub-segment, the Industrial Internet of Things (IIoT), will digitally orchestrate factory floors, physical products, workers and all enterprise functions and processes, unleashing enormous value potential.

Beyond the Product: Outcomes and Value

In only a few years time we will look back and call the two decades since the turn of the century the period of "the end of the product." Ever more advanced digital technology will help to establish a new world in which customers will ask businesses for complex "outcomes" delivered by digital services around physical products instead of delivery of mere hardware.

The software "tissue" and data analytics that will eventually permeate the industrial sector will create a very distinctive new stage of economy. Enterprises will have departed from a conventional focus on manufacturing "dumb" low-margin products made for anonymous markets to forming very personalized relationships with their customers, driven by the latter's instantaneous demand for "switched-on," software-connected, and eventually even Living Products and Living Services with huge value potential. Digital technology will also enable providers of outcomes to monitor the shape of outcomes and usage patterns in the field.

In the churn of this megatrend, the terms B2B and B2C will start to blur. In fact it will be one of the defining fascinations of the industrial sector's digitization that enterprises used to dealing with business clients will suddenly be forced to think like consumer-facing businesses as part of the trend known as "industrial consumerism." This means, that, for not only consumer goods companies but B2B industrial companies too, final outcome experience and service quality will now be the top criteria for success or failure – and eventually the only significant source of corporate value in this sector.

This is driven by a shift in customer attitudes and, as such, is a clear rebuke to the common assumption in government that it is businesses that will drive the broad-based trend towards digitization. What we currently see is the opposite: the urge for change clearly stems from the demand not the supply side.

It is the phenomenon of industrial consumerism and the emergence of Living Products that are driving the change. In that regard many governments are too focused on creating the right environment for digitizing the shop floor, not realizing that this is not the right starting point for enterprises to arrive at the necessary new business models.

In only a short while we will be accustomed to markets in which tried-and-tested industrial hardware products will become permanently reconfigurable software containers, eclipsed in profitability by their own new service qualities.

This will have dramatic effects for businesses and how they go about managing their products. This will be when companies immerse themselves in ecosystems and alliances with what today would seem unlikely partners – another seismic shift for most of today's industrial organizations.

It will therefore be paramount for industrial companies to master this radical transition successfully, opening themselves to a journey that will change their operating models, ways of working and organization beyond recognition – the alternative being a catastrophic loss of market clout and profitability.

This is why this book's aim is to familiarize business leaders from the industrial sectors with the key competencies necessary to tackle all this – competencies such as creating unified Product Lifecycle Management (PLM), embedding software and connectivity in products and services, using analytics to drive value and growth, creating closed-loop agility in development and manufacturing, selling "as a service" and orchestrating the digital and industrial ecosystem, to name but a few.

Two Battlegrounds, Trapped Value and Six "No-Regrets"

From the perspective of industrial enterprises, digital disruption will have two major battlegrounds. On the one hand, it will be about leveraging new digital technologies to bolster internal efficiency throughout all functions, as only this will fund expansion into current and future markets around Living Products. Buried value can be found plentifully, especially in legacy industrial businesses, and digital technology can typically bring it to light for investment into the future.

On the other hand, digitization will challenge businesses to work out how Living Products with a smart software lifeblood can make a market, how an advanced, technology-driven and value-creating digital customer relationship could look, and how it can be embedded into new and unaccustomed outcome models.

Both fields currently probably appear to many business leaders like giant construction sites with no horizon, with works in constant progress because the technologies deployed are incessantly evolving. Which one should one pick, when and along which roadmap? This sort of disorientation might even repel enterprises and their executives to the point of postponing work or even giving up completely on attempting a future-proof digital strategy.

Certainly at the moment, the progress of IIoT adoption is sluggish. Research conducted for the World Economic Forum showed 72 percent of the C-level executives interviewed were convinced that the IIoT would fundamentally change their industry, but just 20 percent had a thought-through strategy for harnessing it.[2]

The dizzying vortex is not just because of digital technology's swift advances. It is also the ever-complicating mix of numerous underlying technologies such as sensors, cloud computing, processing power, business intelligence algorithms, robots, artificial intelligence, cognitive computing and big data.

The decision to give this book the title "Industry X.0" was born not least from the awareness that technology now is in such dynamic flux that its staging posts can no longer be pinned down for longer than a moment. Industry 4.0 will turn swiftly to 5.0, to 6.0, and counting.

Still, in the middle of this raging tech storm there exists a bedrock foundation of digital models, mantras and measures that will create immediate value in any industrial enterprise. A company that adopts them and makes them work adequately will be steering the right digital course regardless of what the future holds and which trajectories digital technology takes.

This is the upside of the current technology frenzy, the opportunity for "unconventional" growth, the chance for industrial businesses that execute their digital strategy right to reap unheard-of speeds of profitable expansion. I think there is every reason to believe the landslide successes of digitally driven businesses such as Amazon or Facebook can be replicated in the industrial sphere.

Those software-only platforms can be a role model for many industrial products. Not all products can be transformed into platforms, but certainly sooner or later every industrial product will be integrated into another product that operates as a platform.

To be as helpful as possible to industrial practitioners, this book is therefore built around a set of fundamental digital "no-regret" capabilities every company should implement and use as a launch pad for digitization. They form the basis for a detailed, strategic *tour d'horizon* showing what the industrial sector will face over the coming years and how to harness it.

Fluidity and Data Pervasiveness Across the Enterprise

Often referred to as the "fourth industrial revolution," and better framed as "Industry X.0," the digital transformation of industrial companies has profound ramifications for businesses' cost structure, their work process design, the involvement of human labor and, crucially, the shaping of products and services.

Digitization is not – by far – only just about the progressive automation of existing manufacturing facilities and shop floors. Casting the net much wider, it entails completely new digital set-ups across all business functions and the creation of holistic new operating models around software-enabled connected products.

Thus, internally, enterprise digitization covers any process or operation that does not involve direct consumer interaction – areas such as idea generation, testing and prototyping, or R&D, with the management of customer, supplier and partner relationships also crucially defined by the new digital ways of steering industrial production.

Externally, business digitization means hunting for propositions that customers find attractive because they offer excellent software-induced efficiency or convenience, fulfill an outcome or create good value for their own business.

Creating agility and acceleration of processes is hence among the top three commandments for a solid digital strategy. Industrial businesses' product and service development units must be enabled to react in real-time to changes in the market. And in a demand-driven economy, they must be able to hyperpersonalize a product or service in a short timeframe, down to a lot of just one.

This radical shift is only achievable when, among other measures, siloed units within the enterprise are broken up and unhindered information loops are established to connect designers with engineers with marketers with customers with suppliers with boardrooms. An absolute maximum of data pervasiveness but also much more decentralized decision-making processes based on local data analysis will define the well digitized organizations of the future.

Innovation in the New and in the Core – Finding the Right Pivot

Importantly, a dual innovation approach will usually be needed. Most industrial companies still run very profitable legacy product or service lines that need to be maintained while applying gradual innovation steps. In a completely separate strand, a second innovation engine for thinking "outside the box" must be kick-started to come up with new and visionary data-based customer propositions unrelated to the old world. This is going to require some extra human and financial resources.

What this implies – applying ingenuity at different speeds and looking at different technological horizons within one business – is certainly not easy to achieve, but it is a necessity for success in a hyper-connected corporate future. Eventually and over time both innovation streams will need to be led to new and future-proofed business models.

What customers want and expect, are no longer just bigger, better, faster or smaller products and services. Rather it is ideally up to industrial businesses to anticipate through their intimate digital customer relationships what their customers and the customers of their customers require. The "why behind the buy" has to be understood and this requires a new, demand-driven approach to innovation, one open to external input from extended ecosystems and banking heavily on digital feedback loops with the end-user market.

The trends described will also have a massive impact on the way the whole product value chain and product engineers, factory staff and field agents work. From their perspective, incorporating and blending with intelligent machinery and software tools will be the birth of the connected industrial workforce.

Digital technology will augment employees in all functions across a business. Shop-floor employees will eventually cooperate with semi-autonomous machines at very close distance in a state of mutual understanding. They will wear data-collecting devices such as smart glasses or helmets, augmenting their skills to achieve much better productivity. Product engineers will be supported by artificial intelligence (AI) driven software and generative designs. AI will even take a seat in the boardroom, supporting strategic management decisions.

This new work style and work environment will require new training and re-skilling. This holds true for blue- and white-collar workers, managers and executives. Overall, enterprises will have to prepare by adopting a more active role in training, developing and preparing existing staff for the digital age or else suffer a significant skills shortage.

Tying Together Products, Ecosystems and Platform Products

Finally, the IIoT requires that input from customers, subcontractors, partners and suppliers be channelled to continually influence strategy throughout a product's lifecycle. Leveraging allied ecosystem parties is therefore becoming critical to arrive at satisfactory time-to-capability, agility-to-assemble and speed-to-market. And on top of that it will also blur traditional industry boundaries.

Building an ecosystem is a skilful task, requiring business leaders to think laterally, factoring in wide horizons of possible allies and unusual business cases and opportunities. This is a drastic departure from old-style product-focused manufacturing, but is still rewarding and will create enormous value.

Against this ecosystem backdrop, many industrial products will be shaped to become platforms. The trailblazers here are the likes of Apple and Google. Both businesses created an ecosystem-style developer community around their smartphone operating systems as platforms. External app creators are the ones imbuing otherwise "dumb" smartphones with value – to the mutual benefit of all: the developer, the platform owner and the customer. Again, there is no reason to assume that industrial companies cannot replicate a similarly stellar success around mining trucks, jet engines or home technology such as lighting, security or heating systems – though surely not all industrial products can turn into platform products.

How to Use This Book

As is probably already clear, the huge changes digitization is set to bring about in manufacturing can be as bewildering as they are fascinating. This book has been written to be your guide to this new territory. The landscape is wildly complex, but, if you know how to read them, its multitude of features provide compelling pointers for the future.

Think of this, then, as something to be *used* – a usage manual, if you like, for the Industrial Internet of Things (IIoT). While it may serve as a general-interest primer, it is aimed mainly at those who will be actively implementing the change. It provides a clear delineation of the challenges and opportunities, and invaluable guidelines on drawing up the right digitization roadmap for your organization. Not all routes will be the same.

And just as there is no fixed path towards the digitized industrial future, there is no one route through this book. Read it in order, or zero in on particular areas as you require. In this, you can be guided by this section.

Be aware that each chapter can be read independently and that what is discussed in them is illustrated by company cases and with the key takeaways.

Part I, comprising Chapters 1-3, is your introductory overview of the IIoT transformation, designed to help you orient yourself in the new world. Chapter 1 gives the current big picture. I look at the flurry of massively disruptive new technologies converging to create the IIoT and explain how the result will be an entirely unprecedented paradigm of manufacturing in which businesses will operate in highly unfamiliar ways. Chapter 2 shows where we're headed, explaining how the IIoT will inevitably lead to a new kind of economy, the Outcome Economy. Chapter 3 discusses the enormous value to be gained from digitization of industry.

Part II, comprising Chapters 4-9, is a series of detailed looks at the key areas a digitization strategy will need to encompass. Chapter 4 gets you started on your path towards digitization. It introduces six "no-regret" capabilities – digitally-based changes you can make now that are certain to deliver results. Chapter 5 looks at big (and ever-increasing) data, probably the single most powerful value driver in the Industry X.0 – as long as you get your data analytics right. Chapter 6 takes you through digital product development, discussing the importance of strengthening software capabilities, synchronizing software and hardware clocks, and of having a robust Digital Product Lifecycle Management (DPLM). Chapter 7 highlights the challenges of managing the human workforce in the era of roboticization and artificial intelligence. Chapter 8 is your guide to innovation in the radical new world of the IIoT, describing the four main innovator types and explaining why only one can really thrive in the Outcome Economy. Chapter 9 explains how in the IIoT's porous, interconnected world, you will need to become part of an ecosystem and may well benefit from building a platform.

Part III, Chapter 10 is a look further into the future, to 2030 and beyond, at a magical, ultra-fluid world in which products can change shape and the Outcome Economy gives way to the Pull Economy.

At the end of the book you will find all the chapter takeaways – that provide a quick and easy access to the actions needed to be taken to digitize your business –, a glossary of terms and an index.

Too Much Will be Lost by Sitting on the Fence

Arguing the case for digitization in the face of scepticism from staff, investors and business partners may take ingenuity, courage, stamina and lots of skills in change management on the part of executives and business leaders. It is all worth it and there is no alternative.

The ground is shifting, but the industrial world's rapid digital transformation should not to be seen as a threat. It is a major opportunity for value creation, not to mention for an incredibly dynamic and stimulating work environment. Industrial companies should seize it rather than wait and see – or risk becoming a digital laggard, resulting in low margins, weak innovation power, slow profits and even disappearance from the market.

There is, contrastingly, little to fear from making a start at digitization if you take the right approach. You can and in fact should start small, scaling swiftly only if your initiative proves successful. That is the beauty of the digital era.

PART I

The Industrial Internet of Things – Transforming Manufacturing Beyond Recognition

Chapter 1

Industry's Ongoing and Accelerating Digital Transformation

Smartened-up and tightly connected industrial manufacturing processes are going to go mainstream in just a few years in all advanced markets and many emerging ones. A sub-segment of the Internet of Things, the Industrial Internet of Things (IIoT), will digitally orchestrate factory floors, physical products, workers and more, unleashing enormous value. However, critical to the success of this new world will be deployment of the right technology, orchestration of it in the right way, the embedding of enterprises in the right ecosystems of business partners, and last but not least, finding adequately skilled people.

As is already fairly common knowledge, the Internet of Things (IoT) put very simply refers to appliances networked via digitization. Most readers will have at least a nodding acquaintance with some common examples, whether by reputation or direct experience: cars, toasters, fridges and central heating systems that can be monitored and controlled from household computers and smartphones.

The Industrial Internet of Things is a key subset within the IoT, less visible than our common household objects, but with arguably far greater power to revolutionize the way the world works. It creates, via connected technologies and various platforms, highly efficient relationships between products, machines, services, and sites, but also between customers, workers, managers, suppliers and partners.

It is, in short, the main bridge between the physical and digital enterprise applications enabled by the so called "fourth industrial revolution" – that is, the revolution in industry brought about by digital technology. This is really many revolutions in one, comprising various advances such as artificial intelligence, robots, big data analytics and, in the pipeline, quantum computing.

The combinatorial effect of all these (Figure 1.1) is unprecedentedly seismic, probably the single most dramatic cataclysm in consumer and business goods manufacturing in human history, overhauling practically every business conviction generally held dear, whether in resource allocation, production process sequencing, materials handling, workforce involvement, customer relationship or environmental management.

In a way, it is tempting to see the IIoT as actually *synonymous* with the fourth industrial revolution because it does so much to unify all the innovations by networking them. However, as the other examples I've given indicate, it is by no means the whole revolution on

Figure 1.1 – Combinatorial Effect of Technology[1]

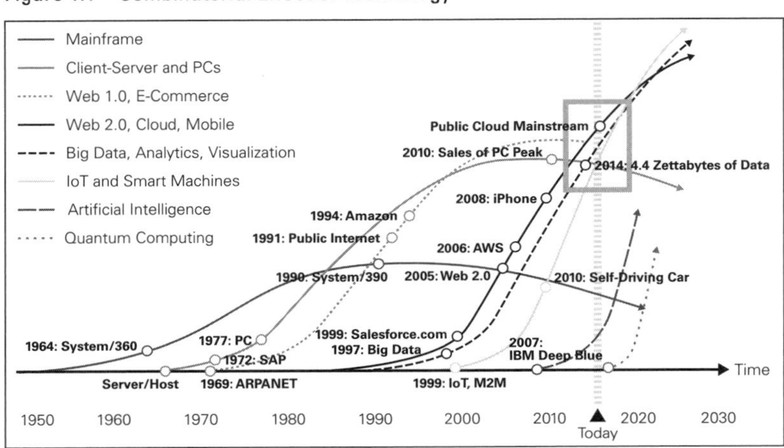

its own. The IIoT is, if you like, what turbocharges the combinatorial effect of these already wildly disruptive technologies by seeing them work in concert.

This book is not a comprehensive guide to the entire fourth industrial revolution – to every node of technological change that comprises it. Its focus is very much the IIoT. However, precisely because the IIoT connects the other factors, it offers a key route into understanding how to capitalize upon the whole and avoid being left behind.

In particular, I will look at the innovations in connectivity and data collection that enable the IIoT alone: tech such as sensors, portable devices, the cloud, application programme interfaces (APIs) and apps. These are exploding.

All this is set to shake up research and development, manufacturing, aftersales, and product and service configurations. In numerous industrial settings, the drift, albeit often tentative, has already begun towards digitally run shop floors, management processes, platforms and ecosystems.

This opens up space to establish new income streams for enterprises and allows companies to set a strategic course for entirely new business models focused on delivering quality "outcomes" for customers rather than just physical products.

Outcomes are another reason why the emergence of the IIoT is an event of such historical significance. It marks the end of roughly 200 years of modern industrial production habits because it relegates basic products to insignificance compared to the results they deliver at any given moment thanks to their digital connectivity.

We are right at the tipping point of this change and there is simply no better time to be getting to grips with it. The entire purpose of this book is to help you do this. In this chapter I will further delineate the significance of the IIoT, giving a sense of the (relatively early) stage of development it is at now.

Finally, as a sort of summary overview of the other chapters in this book, I will sketch out some key steps you need to take and concepts you need to understand to correctly position your company in the IIoT's radically new landscape.

The Drivers of Change in the Industrial Sphere

The connected, smart product is at the core of the change. The combination of smart products, services and new experiences will disrupt legacy business models and shake up the entire product value chain.

Before we go any further, let's lay out the key drivers leading the move towards the IIoT (Figure 1.2).

Figure 1.2 – The Drivers for Change in the Industrial Landscape[2]

Sensors	Devices	Networks	APIs	Apps	Data
212bn	**50bn**	**2.3bn**	**75%**	**4.4bn**	**52EB**
Sensors Expected by 2020	Devices Expected by 2020	People Accessing 4G-LTE Networks by 2020	Fortune 1000 Could Offer Public	Total Number of App Users by 2017	Mobile Data Traffic per Month by 2021
Location			Billing	Touch Interfaces	User Data
Motion			Mapping	Gesture Tracking	Transaction Data
Chemical			Social	Augmented Reality	Field Data
Light		NFC	Search	Voice Recognition	Inventory Data
Heat		4G LTE	Marketing		Performance Data
Sound					
IoT Enablers				IoT Value Drivers	

1. Pervasiveness of connected technology creates context. As shown in Figure 1.2, sensors, connectivity, APIs and data in products at commodity price levels will drive new levels of intelligence in smart products.

2. Platforms and data for optimization. Smart products, pushed to become Living Products by sophisticated embedded software, will be connected to platforms during operations and accompanied with analytics and data-driven services to optimize their operation.

3. Ecosystems and services drive value. Data and services provided by smart products and platform ecosystem allow creation of mutually complementing value-add services and new revenue streams while the smart product is in operation.

4. Hyperpersonalization and new experiences disrupt. Smart products have the ability to hyperpersonalize, adapting to the individual product user in his or her individual context with the objective of optimizing the business outcome. Hyperpersonalization creates new experiences for the individual. This leads to a new level of competition around the combination of smart products, services and new experiences, potentially disruptive to existing business models.

5. As-a-service business models emerge. Consumption-based business models replace traditional "sell-and-maintain" business models. This involves significant changes to the balance sheet with CAPEX shifting from customer to the as-a-service provider.

6. New technologies will disrupt further. Robotics, autonomous systems, artificial intelligence and deep learning, augmented and virtual reality, 5G networks, 3/4D Printing, blockchain, and other new technologies will reach industrial strength and radically impact the way products are engineered, manufactured and operated.

7. Security and data privacy ensure resilience and fairness. Progress in industrial-strength security, data ownership and sharing, and data privacy solutions are a prerequisite for the IIoT. Security solutions will be engineered to provide resilience during cyber attacks and new principles around data sharing will ensure fairness between stakeholders.

Technology Becomes Affordable and Puts Speed Behind the IIoT

Why is the current moment in the development of the IIoT so crucial? Because of the standard pattern by which innovations often reach maturity and marketability: IIoT technology has simultaneously become cheaper and its sophistication has increased, making it ready to go mainstream.

Production costs and market prices have tumbled to commodity levels over the last two decades or so for many technologies critical to the IIoT: cloud computing services, processing power, storage space, analytics tools, mobile connectivity, and components such as sensors. Prices have fallen by up to a factor of 50 compared to only a few years ago (see Figure 1.3). Concurrently, new waves of innovation have succeeded their predecessors with exceptional and increasing speed, shortening the window within which to absorb and adapt to the changes.

Figure 1.3 – A Decade of Eroding Cost Fuels the Rise of the Internet of Things[3]

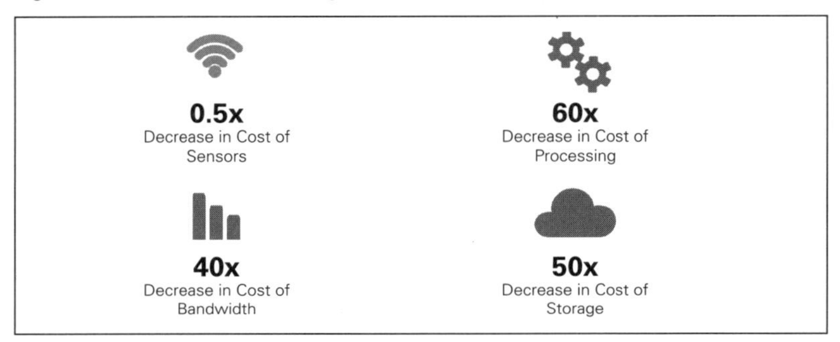

All this greatly increases both the feasibility and attractiveness of new investment cases unthinkable only a few years ago. A small ironmonger operating an assembly line in an urban backyard, for instance, can now buy software-controlled sensor kits to apply a basic form of predictive analytics for lathe maintenance or managing energy consumption.

Such small-scale entrepreneurs will probably soon be using process engineering equipment that, not long ago, existed only in research laboratories or would have cost a fortune to integrate into ordinary factory floors.

The potential for rendering old-style enterprise arrangements smart from end-to-end, then, is huge. Research anticipates that around two thirds of today's companies can easily boost efficiency and value via a gradual introduction of digitized processes, as many of their departments have barely been put on a digital footing at all over the last decades. This will soon streamline and optimize businesses around the world and pump trillions of dollars of income into the economy.

In that perspectie the IIoT is probably the greatest compound value proposition industrial manufacturers have ever been offered.

The Value of the IIoT is Still to be Unlocked

One can get a sense of the IIoT's potential for value creation by looking at where the new smart technology is already embedded in efficient set-ups. Advantages such as greater visibility of processes, much more efficient data utilization, and the intertwining of underlying systems and sub-processes can boost unit cost ratios, workforce flexibility and product quality by several orders of magnitude.

Consider the technology known as Predictive Maintenance: data is collected from machinery and used to predict future maintenance stops. This helps to save up to 12 percent in repair costs and reduces overall maintenance cost by up to 30 percent.[4]

Or take predictive analytics, born of machine-installed sensors and intelligent diagnostic software, which reduces machine breakdowns by a whopping 70 percent.[5] Hardly any previous technological advance has been able boast productivity gains of this magnitude.

The big picture estimates are at least equally stunning. By adopting digitally controlled business and manufacturing processes, global factories are set to secure $100tn of combined value for society and industry by 2025.[6]

This should even make manufacturing sufficiently competitive for substantial operations to be relocated from the lower-cost emerging world back to highly industrialized western countries. That should push new-growth nations to quickly develop their own digital industrial base in order to remain competitive. More generally, it's a clear indication that no one can afford to ignore the onward march of the IIoT.

The few early-adopters who are significantly realizing IIoT – aircraft or car manufacturers and mining operators being good examples – already significantly realizing IIoT enjoy higher productivity, lower operational costs, better working conditions, and effective machine occupancy. They are experiencing a significant profit uplift.[7]

Figure 1.4 – Digital Index and Financial Performance of German Industrial Players[8]

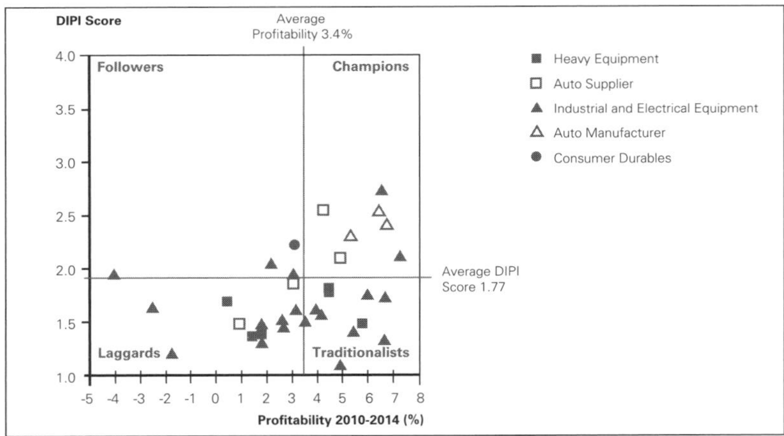

Ecosystems Form Powerful Wells of Innovation

While many of my remarks already suggest this, I should emphasize that deploying smart manufacturing solutions yields a lot more than just a few insular, one-dimensional efficiency gains reflected in profit and loss accounts. This is precisely because the IIoT is itself multi-dimensional, comprising so many innovations in concert.

Compared with individual innovations, the network effect here means that the value horizon is exponentially larger and vastly more transformative. Technological transformation is the basis, but it leads, as inevitably as water flowing downhill, to interconnected changes in products, services, strategies, processes and, crucially, relationships between businesses and sectors.

Smart manufacturing will, by definition, not evolve in the form of isolated beacon projects. It is the nature of these radical new production set-ups to emerge in sector context – thriving best in expanding ecosystems within and across industries.

In other words, the innovations that work in concert will be achieved through and give rise to innovation *processes* that also happen in concert. The more adequate and user experience-oriented IIoT technology you and your partners have in your process chains, components and products, the more everyone will be able to introduce new business models based on service offerings that mutually augment physical products and tap collectively into new revenue streams.

As you phase in IIoT-enabled processes, you will have no choice but to open up your existing business model step by step in thorough and irreversible ways. Your enterprise will eventually be embedded in a myriad of flexibly evolving digital relationships with other parties. Your own digitization's pace will depend on the ebb and flow of your customers', partners', and suppliers' parallel processes. You will, in short, have to get used to progress in step with your various ecosystem partners.

Managing such ecosystems, harnessing Open Innovation flows among their constituents and breaking down silos, will thus become critical capabilities for business leaders. Competition to be part of the best-performing ecosystems will almost certainly be even stronger than the rivalry around individual product markets.

Following this path, you will eventually build the capacity to morph from a more traditional product-oriented manufacturer into a provider of measurable outcomes: complex bundles of services, hardware, and experience.

The Product of Me vs. Mass Manufacturing

Key to the new, digitally enhanced Outcome Economy will be stronger customer relationships than any yet imagined. As is explained in the next chapter in detail, your company will eventually face an environment in which the concept of a mass-market for a mass-product is under increasing pressure.

You will no longer discover and calculate potential market niches for a certain product in advance according to the age-old practice of prospective market research. Rather, you will use digitally agile manufacturing to make a product in direct response to concrete demand, even for small lot numbers

In fact, the demand may be from just one customer for one thing. The "lot size one" or so-called "product of me" is among the most defining elements of the IIoT. As a result of the process known as "hyperpersonalization," customers will be able to demand and order anything from a car to a toaster to a mining solution significantly more tailored to their needs than is possible today.

The product of me also means a product highly adaptable to different uses and users. Software-enabled, it can match, by functional adaptation, the various needs and situations with which its user is confronted. But a product can also be highly adaptable, through intelligent digital user interfaces, to various humans working with it. Overall, hardware products of all sorts are going to be configured by way of software to maximize user experience.

Liquid Fulfillment Networks Will Supplant Old-Style Factories

The trend towards this advanced form of manufacturing management is clearly underway and seems unstoppable, but it will be some time before most of today's manufacturers reach it.

How will it work? The new, very fluid enterprise set-ups will be dominated by far-reaching machine intelligence, and highly automated and fluid production processes, embedded in what I call "fulfillment networks" – multi-sourced catchment areas for components and services that feed through your manufacturing process. The incoming parts and materials will interact automatically with the intelligent machines to manage the cost-effective assembly of customized products.

By applying analytics to the data generated, the machines will be able to identify and predict performance bottlenecks and make smarter decisions about how to improve factory operations, manage workforce and supply chain risks, and enhance the product design process.

Manufacturers will have to open up to technology set-ups and process configurations that they are not used to and never had a chance to test-drive. But as products become more connected and software-intelligent, so too will the factory floors creating them.

The solid basis for success within the world of the IIoT will be exploratory new watertight business cases, extracted from realistic use cases so that the return on investments can be easily identified and measured.

After all, bringing the IIoT to life will come at a cost. Modernizing IT systems and retrofitting equipment with sensor technology can be a substantial expense, as can the completely new facilities for which some manufacturers may opt.

Most traditional machine control systems are proprietary, often developed in-house decades ago. The technology in many cases turns out to be hermetically insular and difficult to turn interoperable. Substantial investment will therefore be needed to allow it to participate in free-flowing open technology ecosystems in which suppliers and even customers turn into a permanent source of data signals influencing manufacturing processes.

In many cases, systems for operations, planning and engineering may also be contained in separate silos, making it difficult to integrate new processes even when the companies in question have already adopted technologies that make it easier to integrate supporting systems.

What's more, upgrading and retrofitting existing enterprise infrastructure will be done progressively over time at a stretched-out cost profile. At a certain stage, the advantages of connected machines on the factory floor – speed of operations, flexibility in customization, improved operating performance, faster response to consumer demand, cost reduction – will reveal their innate financial advantage and the investment will break even.

Let's also not forget that there are immediate savings to be achieved with minimal investments in existing infrastructure. A water utility company catering for a large capital city, for example, introduced digital infrastructure to better monitor its water flows and pipe system.[9] It thus reduced its operating expenses (OPEX) by up to eight percent in areas served by the new analytics, while averting up to 12 percent on capital expenditure (CAPEX) by relieving existing capacity.[10]

Or take the aerospace and defense manufacturer which, using similar means, was able to bring down the error rate of staff installing plane seats by an incredible 100 percent, while the time needed for the task was cut to a sixth.

In addition, there are more and more new industrial data platforms, the role of which I will introduce in detail in Chapter 9. These software service bundles – prominent examples being MindSphere from Siemens and Microsoft's Azure – can ultimately put your business on a digital footing end-to-end, but may be switched on bit by bit if necessary. These services' big advantage is that they help you orchestrate your own processes by creating a backbone holding everything together – from supply chain to research and development to manufacturing to aftersales. At the same time, they allow you to connect to your customers – for instance through connected products.

The Critical Importance of Preparing the Digital Workforce

An IIoT-embedded workforce will work in a state of much greater fluidity than today. Connected equipment, devices and wearables can help staff interact with their machines and work together in new ways.

Accenture has, for example, created a use case around an augmented reality solution for workers. Product engineers can act simultaneously from different locations on a virtual product that they all see via wearables. Each participant sees what the others do on a 3D digital model of the product and can then react or cooperate accordingly.

Automation will accelerate dramatically in IIoT environments, changing the face of the manufacturing workforce as well, including the skill profiles required to succeed. More complex skills such as equipment development, maintenance and repair will be in demand.

Surveys show that manufacturing executives expect human-machine-centric environments to be commonplace in plants by 2020 – and they recognize the benefits.[11]

Creating a blended workforce in which humans and robot machines collaborate dynamically can deliver outcomes that neither could produce alone and do so at much higher levels of efficiency.

New technologies will to some extent allow manufacturers to harvest the skills and job candidates needed globally to some extent. But enterprises' ability to manage the re-skilling and retraining of their workforce in the digital age will be a critical determinant of how swiftly they adopt these technologies. To make all this a success as the new technologies take hold, change managers will be in demand to help the workforce make the huge adaptation to new work set-ups and cooperation styles.

The Surprisingly Slow Embrace of the IIoT by Business

Given the potential, it is notable that the IIoT still seems to be something of an unknown quantity to most strategic corporate thinkers. Many continue to base their success on trusted and profitable legacy technology architecture and process arrangements that are often decades-old.

There is an interesting contradiction here. Research conducted by the World Economic Forum show that 84 percent of business leaders expect the IIoT to disrupt their operating models within the next five years. Yet only seven percent of these have a comprehensive IIoT strategy in place, while a staggering 73 percent admit to having none at all. It seems that while executives are fully aware in the abstract of the IIoT's potential, most find the actuality extremely daunting, to say the least.[12]

Figure 1.5 – Putting New Technologies to Work in Industry X.0[13]

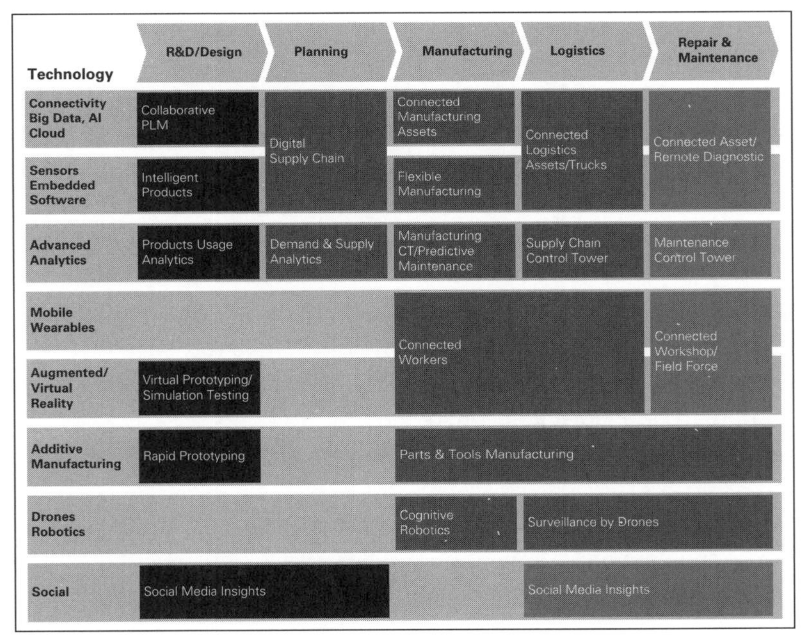

In many ways, this is actually not so surprising. Entire smart factories, let alone smartened-up sectors, will obviously be hugely complex and radically different from what we now know – ultimately ecosystems of production processes that are distributed, self-organizing, software-intelligent, highly automated, platform-based and demand-driven.

In my view, this kind of sophistication is still years away, even in highly industrialized economies. And then there's the added complexity of radically new business models and processes that result from all this, as I've just described in the previous two sections.

So executives are right to be cautious and even to take their time, but this should in no way translate to sitting on their hands. Remember those seven percent who *do* have a comprehensive IIoT plan and keep your eye on them. The change is happening and the manufacturers who start to align operational and informational technology soonest will be best positioned to take full advantage of it.

Different companies from different industries naturally progress at differing levels of speed and boldness. Domestic appliance and home technology makers are just about to discover the huge advantages of embedding software on a large scale in their manufacturing and products. In contrast, the aerospace and industrial engineering industries are well advanced at sensorization and data analysis, resulting from safety regulation requirements in these sectors early on. A new plane model by aircraft maker Airbus has around 20,000 individual sensors in its wings,[14] while GE's new jet engines collect 5,000 data points per second.[15]

Businesses that have successfully reaped value from new technology in the past often tend to be similarly meticulous about planning for and adopting further innovations. In car production, the legacy of finding efficiency gains in cutting-edge production set-ups goes right back to Ford's famous Model T, the first assembly-line car ever, launched in 1908.[16] Car producers continue to be at the vanguard when it comes to the IIoT due to the high degree of automated production they achieved in a major mechanization push as early as the 1970s. However, there are still significant productivity gains to unlock as we will see in Chapter 3.

By the way, research regarding the current leaders and laggards here reveals a striking geographic pattern: US and, to some extent, Asian firms consider themselves well-grounded in digital leader roles, with a sound basis for further investment. European enterprises, on the other hand, see their sectors trailing. That can to my mind be seen as just a perception. In general, all countries still have a lot to do to help their businesses unlock value.

Figure 1.6 – Assessment of Industry Digitization by Geography[17]

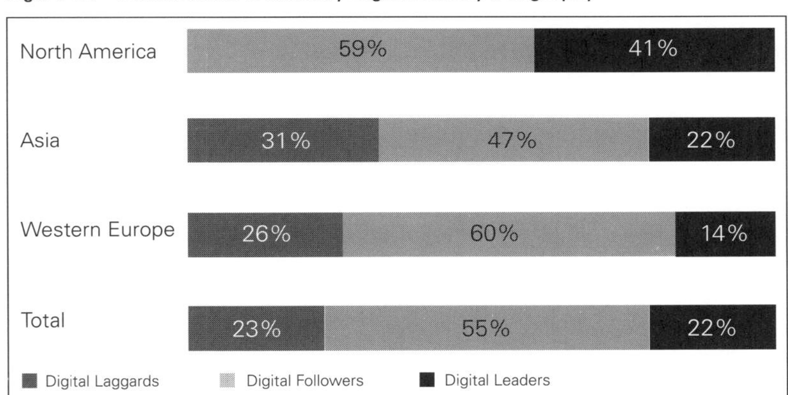

At any rate, the enticement of massive efficiency gains makes it largely inevitable that other sectors will catch up soon and *en masse*. Where equipment is unconnected, where it is fixed only when it breaks, and where maintenance stops are scheduled not according to load or usage but along fixed intervals, the unpredictability is costly – financially and in terms of customer reputation.

Already, even outside the vanguard sectors, the first few insular modules have appeared on many industrial shop floors, throughout enterprise operations and functions and even within a few consumer product ranges. Mostly piecemeal, these connected setups still await the effective and consistent orchestration of full IIoT integration. Yet even in this direction, steps have been taken. In some instances, operational production technology has already been connected to IT business backbones – one of the most defining decisions to be taken in building up IIoT structures within enterprises.

Meanwhile, embedded sensors and numerical steering now control most newly built machinery in industrial engineering, regardless of the sector. Even some elementary smart production elements are already in place, allowing a limited degree of timely and continuous visibility into production.

Mechanical engineering giant Siemens, for instance, operates a small electronics plant in Amberg, Germany. In 1990, 25 percent of its processes were automated. Today it is 75 percent. The efficiency advantages are obvious: defect rates have dropped to below 12 per million produced items and output has increased by a factor of 8.5, with little change in employee numbers.[18]

First steps of this kind secure a degree of seamless data flow, forming the basis for machines to become data-linked across the whole process chain – from inventories to design and development units, manufacturing management, supply-chain logistics, enterprise planning systems and, increasingly, also software-bearing products.

And first steps are what concern us here. Perhaps, rather than being intimidated by the vanguard sectors and businesses, we can learn from their approach. The initial lesson is that the small and the simple is the foundation for the large and complex. The most important practical advice regarding the IIoT: take baby steps rather than giant leaps and follow a roadmap flexible enough to let you change course when you need to. There is more than one path to the IIoT and the future of technological development is, of course, unwritten.

Takeaways

1. The industrial sphere is undergoing a profound, even dramatic change. Its drivers are many, among them the pervasiveness of connected technology, platforms and data optimization, hyper-personalization, and as-a-service business models. And we are just at the beginning of the change.

2. Tightly connected industrial manufacturing processes are going to go mainstream soon. The Industrial Internet of Things (IIoT), will digitally orchestrate factory floors, physical products, workers and more, unleashing enormous value.

3. Critical to success in this new digital industrial world will be the deployment of the right technology, preparation of the digital workforce, intelligent orchestration of both, and embedding of enterprises in the right ecosystems of business partners.

Chapter 2

How the IIoT Leads to the Outcome Economy

The Industrial Internet of Things (IIoT) has ripple effects way beyond innovation on factory floors alone. It will drastically change the way companies work with each other and sell to customers. It is no exaggeration to say that this will result in a new kind of economy. In just a few years we will say that the two decades since the turn of the century were "the end of the product." By then we will be accustomed to the newly emerging Outcome Economy in which tried-and-tested industrial hardware products are eclipsed by their much more profitable service qualities. Also called the "usage economy," this will have dramatic effects on businesses and how they manage their products. It will be the era of companies immersing themselves in ecosystems and alliances with unlikely partners.

Looked at from today's perspective, it might sound far-fetched, but eventually all consumers and businesses will want to buy outcomes, not physical hardware. This so-called Outcome Economy is, in its most developed form, still a few years away. However, it is where the IIoT inevitably leads and it is important to have this destination in mind as businesses begin to draw up roadmaps for digitization.

The beginning of this ground-breaking economic approach is already firmly underway in many industrial sectors. Some businesses modelled around it are already proving its viability.

Aircraft engine makers long ago realized that selling ready-to-install engines to airlines and aircraft manufacturers is hard-earned money. Huge research and development cost adds to substantial safety regulatory cost. These can often outweigh profitable sales prices achievable on a very limited market where not enough innovation is happening.

So these manufacturers started selling services based on their products. Under the catchy slogan "power by the hour," they now offer the simple guarantee that an airline's fleet, consisting of X number of aircraft, over a given time period, will have fully maintained engines in full working order, wherever planes are located.

This is not a product but a result – an *outcome* – with a single price tag attached. Airlines love it as it is convenient, predictable and transparent. They know at the beginning of the year exactly what they will spend to run their aircraft for the whole business period – fuel excluded.

And although it is complex to arrange for the sellers, it is still a new and a soon to be profitable source of income for them, saving the overall margin of businesses that was shrinking in pure engine construction.

Though such examples are still insular and a long way from creating an entirely new economic system, they show that the Outcome Economy, is very much in the making.

The cold product turns into something emotional: a customer experience. In our example, the delivery involves not only the provision of a tool to fulfill an end – an engine to get a plane from A to B – but the ongoing guarantee of a working engine, facilitated by delivery of a compound service. In that regard, it is an experience.

New Tech Creates New Business Models

The idea of providing what people want in the shape of an outcome has been around for a while, but has been hard to achieve practically. You often need sensors to know if the outcome is met and to measure your own cost. And you need technology and products that can deliver those outcomes. Specifically, you need sophisticated and affordable devices for measuring service results in a mass market.

The Outcome Economy is becoming a reality because the technology it requires is reaching maturity. Connected sensors make the physical world increasingly quantifiable. Data streams from connected machines and goods provide detailed information about product usage and customer behaviour. By applying advanced analytics to this data, along with external data and domain models, companies can better understand how input variables work together and adjust for better business outcomes.

Precisely quantifiable services also allow for exact prices. This is the trajectory consumer and enterprise markets will take in the future. It is this broad "servitization" of products that will gain ground in all industrial sectors over the coming years, whether con-

Figure 2.1 – Products-as-a-Service Business Models[1]

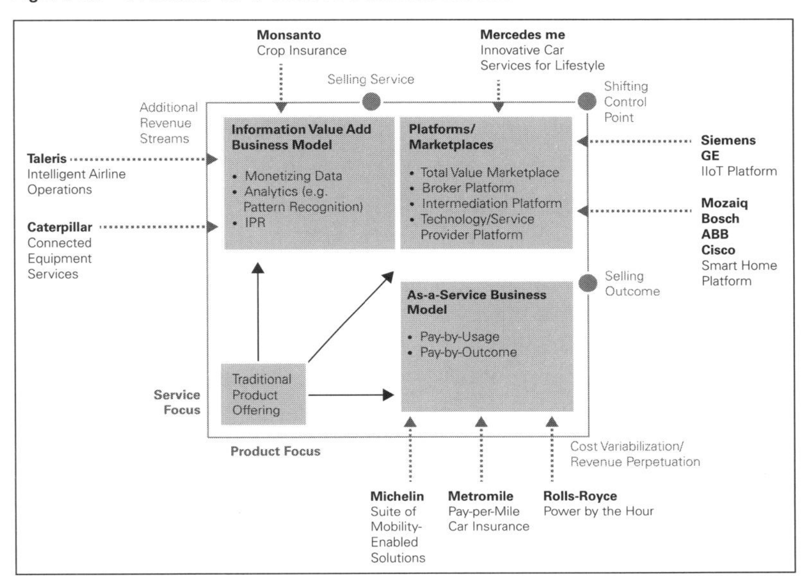

sumer- or business-facing. Once companies prove they can deliver outcomes profitably, it will drive their competitors to do the same.

As the concept gains ground, more and more makers of things will be looking at ways to attach measurable services to their products. Further down the line this will produce more value for the sellers than the hardware product itself ever could. Instead of fighting for market share for one-off sales, the producers will be able to guarantee long-term relationships and, with those, revenue streams.

In a fully-fledged Outcome Economy, power drill manufacturers will price the creation of a hole in the wall and drug producers will promise the outcome of a patient taking a pill at the right frequency, or even simply being cured.

If you base an entire economy on this system you end up with an outcome network in which almost nobody buys a new drill, car, or any other form of physical product. All hardware needed to deliver outcomes will be owned by firms delivering the services. Even they might rent them from third parties in their ecosystem.

That means that the same number of holes will be drilled but with a much smaller number of drills. We can therefore assume that the overall quantity of hardware in the world will shrink and what remains will be used almost constantly at full capacity. Experts also call this type of economy the "usage economy."

A Barclays study forecasts, for example, that autonomous cars, which will reach a share of 50 percent by 2040, could reduce vehicle ownership by 50 percent and each shared driveless car could replace as many as seven traditional vehicles.[2]

It is instantly clear that manufacturing industries, based on pure product design and technology, cannot rely anymore only on pure product design and technology, but will need to find new business models to survive in the long run.

Living Products or the Reinvention of the Product

The journey for businesses in the industrial sector has begun even if they are starting slow and coming from an old world. But as soon as they have smartened their products they will pick up speed and have the means, via data analytics, to push further into what I will call "the New" – the future world of the IIoT, where they will be building platforms around their products, embedding themselves in ecosystems and working towards hyperpersonalized customer experiences.

Figure 2.2 – Industry X.0 Framework[3]

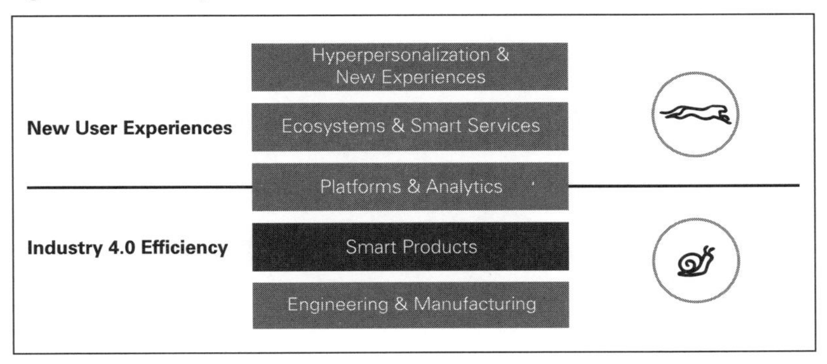

Connected smart products are at the core of the change.

Smart products in smart spaces allow the exploitation of the potential for efficiency and flexibility in engineering and manufacturing. This change can be disruptive through the use of new technologies to fundamentally change the way the product is engineered and manufactured (e.g. 3D Printing, digital twin). Investment upgrades in legacy typically slow down progress.

Smart products will allow for new disruptive business model, and revenue streams. New hyperpersonalized and context-specific user experiences are created through the connection of smart products with platform-based services utilizing the power of broad ecosystems. This change will be fast, disruptive and redefine the rules of competitiveness.

The Outcome Economy will be heavily based on a new notion of the hardware product. Items such as a car or a piece of manufacturing machinery will eventually be a mere container for what is the real value source for maker and user: software-intelligence, enabled by the hardware's platform, brought to life by context-driven user interfaces.

This will be a new world for development engineers and product managers alike. The old concept of unconnected hardware products will be phased out as they fail to earn the necessary margins.

Figure 2.3 – Living Products – The Future of Smart Products[4]

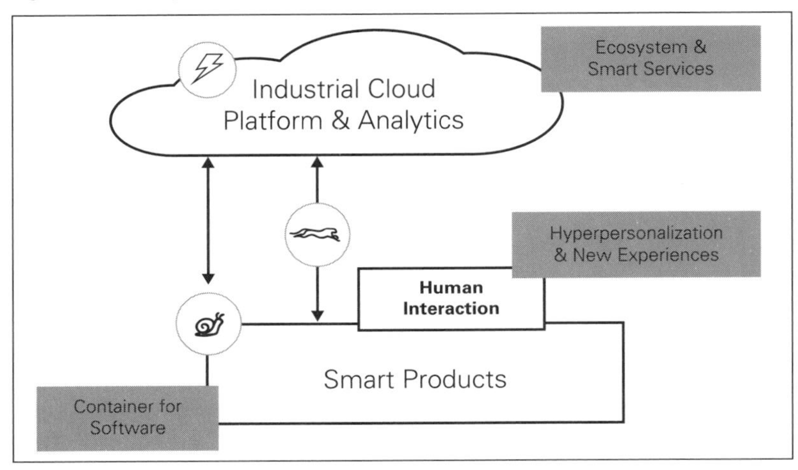

Eventually, powered by more and more technology, such smart or platform products will evolve into Living Products, hardware items so clever and intuitive as to seem to human users like a living organism that can collaborate with them intelligently.

Outcome Orientation Spurs Innovation in Products and Services

Because the outcome concept offers so many possibilities for new ways of thinking about products and services, one can find it being tested in some surprising areas.

For instance, with affordable face-recognition software making inroads into consumer life – from payment systems, to dating websites and border control checks – even measuring laughter can become valuable.

A small comedy club in Barcelona, Spain, has actually tested this. The seat rows at TeatreNeu were fitted with optical sensors recording how often audience members laughed. Each instance of laughter appeared on the bill at a price of 30 cents each. Serious types had a cheap night out, while the easily tickled would have found themselves badly out of pocket if the club had not put a brake on the bill at €24.[5]

The business logic behind this project is far from trivial and provides a model for numerous incumbent industrial groups. Whereas buyers of the service – audience members – can rely on only paying for what they see as quality, the seller might find the "pay for what you eat" model fluid enough to generate more profitable turnover overall – compared with selling complete comedy shows as a bundle of jokes and punch lines.

Thus the Outcome Economy offers a multitude of attractive and flexible new features to both sides of a market. It also helps closed-loop innovation function in a fundamentally new and much more uncompromising way. In our example, gag writers can now perfect their jokes in a really laser-sharp way as they are fed through an immediate feedback loop – creating, for audience members, a better outcome: more laughs.

In the same way, engine makers can innovate by analyzing all the data engines transmit back to them. This gives them a detailed picture of the maintenance requirements created by each airline's usage habits. They can then streamline and tailor their service logistics accordingly.

So, to sum up, outcome-oriented business models force faster innovation and higher individualization. Instantaneous data feedback allows the loop to be closed between real-time use of a product or service and offer development. This creates value because it accelerates development. However, it also requires manufacturers to master multiple development lifecycles running simultaneously at different speeds.

Outcomes are Appearing Across Sectors

In other sectors, mainly business-to-business industries, the outcome concept is quickly gaining ground. Rapid technological advances are helping to propel it to broad adoption.

Take, for instance, medicine. When a doctor prescribes medication, the required outcome is not the pill but that the patient actually takes it and, importantly, gets well. But patients, especially dementia sufferers, often forget their medication. So a company called Proteus Digital Health already in business has inserted a tiny sensor into its pills. This tells a complex IT system whether patients have taken their medication. When they don't, it sends a reminder email or text message.[6]

A few big pharma companies are going beyond the outcome of swallowed pills to focus on the outcome of a cured patient – with revenue coming from the associated savings. This requires carefully crafted partnership networks. One in the works in the US, for instance, involves a pharmacy chain and several payer organizations.

Traditional industrial manufacturers such as French tire maker Michelin have also started to tap into this new approach. Michelin's Effifuel, a service for haulage customers, provides fuel-saving driver education, real-time telematics fleet-control units to monitor driver and truck performance, and tire management in combination with a special low-rolling resistance tire model. Michelin has thus made use of the IIoT to shift from a legacy business of selling tires to selling outcomes. The service can lead to a reduction in fuel consumption of 2.5 liters for every 100 km, representing an average annual saving of $3,300 for long-haul trucks. This amounts to the equivalent of at least a 2.1 percent reduction in total ownership cost for truck fleet operators.[7] The service bundle is so effective that Michelin commits to a firm fuel reduction target and reimburses fees if goals are not met. This is the customer experience dimension I referred to.

Farming is the most recent sector to have adopted outcome-based business models. High-tech agricultural engineering companies have all the data necessary to calculate how many tons of wheat can be produced on a given area of farmland with a particular mix of seed, fertilizer, water, soil chemistry and weather conditions. By combining analytics software with connected tractors, tillers and planters, they can apply the precise mix of seed and fertilizer needed to maximize crop yield. Drones could also be used extensively to monitor the crop and ensure that the right actions are taken with regards to watering, fertilization, and pest deterrence.

Software-intelligent farm machinery can offer very tailored promises. Farmers, will eventually find it very normal and convenient to approach a tractor manufacturer and contract for a specific outcome – eight tons of wheat per hectare by the end of September, say.

In a similar way, a building's management could deliver the outcome of a defined level of energy savings. Sensors, controls and software would analyze the data on when and where people work, adjusting the lighting and temperature levels required.

Dutch lighting specialist Philips, for example, in one of its new service strands, actually sells a certain amount of light rather than bulbs or other luminaires. It retains ownership of the lighting equipment, with customers paying only for the light used. Using high-tech light sources, Philips can carefully adjust the illumination depending on available natural daylight. Customers save energy and costs, and Philips enjoys long-term contracts with them.[8]

This is very much an incomplete list of examples but it shows that digital technology is being used to deliver outcomes at broad levels across industries.

The Why Behind the Buy

As one can see, figure out *why* a customer is buying something from you – the outcome that is their real objective – and you can tailor your offering accordingly.

I've mostly looked at outcomes around products, about how well hardware fulfills its intended purpose. They might relate to operations or maintenance, or savings generated. In general, product outcomes are fairly straightforward because they involve only the product supplier and user.

In the aircraft engine example, product reliability is the outcome customers pay for. The product-service provider, the engine maker, carries the risk of time-on-wing and shop visit cost. This is already a complex proposition, hugely dependent on IIoT capabilities: Rolls-Royce provides a suite of predictive maintenance and repair services for its jet engines, including monitoring engine health and modifying engines to increase reliability and durability.[9]

But there are also more broadly defined business outcomes around quantitative measures. A good example is the business model of airline maintenance specialists. Unlike aircraft engine makers that focus on just one product engine's uptime, those service providers tackle the larger issues of airline delays and cancellations caused by equipment failures. It promises frictionless operation of airline fleets.[10]

To accomplish this outcome, these service providers manage the entire fleet and focus on the entire aircraft, not just the engine. Servicing and maintaining individual aircraft, the company can coordinate overall maintenance schedules. This systemic approach means less disruption, lower costs, better spare-parts inventory management and more satisfied travellers.[11]

This outcome product feeds a lucrative market. Commercial airlines spend about $170bn per year on jet fuel. Estimates within the industry point to around five percent cost reduction from better flight planning and operational changes: a benefit of over $8bn per year.[12]

From Rigid Business Silos to Agile Ecosystems

So how will the Outcome Economy eventually take shape to become, as the term suggests, a true and complete economy? How will previously disconnected businesses interact as interconnected alliance partners to cater for new outcome market segments?

Take the example of outcome-driven tractor manufacturers. In leasing out their huge fleets of software-enabled machinery, they will collect agricultural data at unprecedented resolution. These big-agri data sets will not just be valuable to farmers. They could also be sold to investment firms and brokerage houses to inform positioning in capital markets. In terms of what will come, this is actually a relatively small example, but it shows how complex the new networks can become.

It also serves to illustrate how valuable digital data will be in the era of an outcome-driven economy. Creating data on usage and customer behavior and analyzing it using advanced analytics tools will eventually be as normal in the industrial sector as it is already in service sectors such as banking or retailing.

Actionable data and decisions based on data insights will be the industrial sector's value drivers – whether for achieving better internal operational efficiency or externally finding outcomes that represent even better customer experiences.

Businesses competing on their ability to deliver quantifiable results to customers will rely on business partners, advanced analytics and new data streams from smart products in the field to gain timely insights about customer needs and behaviours. They will, in other words, need to become part of ecosystems.

Few companies, even the world's largest, are in a position to fully own emerging digital value chains. Connected products working in alliance with service provision to deliver outcomes tend, by their nature, to entail collaborative decision-making between different players.

There is no avoiding this. The advantages, will quickly make themselves apparent: speed and agility – crucial in digital markets since they evolve much faster than physical industries. Being part of an ecosystem allows participating companies to specialize in their core competencies and work together to quickly adapt to changes in external environments.

All this is a clear challenge for traditional manufacturers. As digitization and the IIoT drive the shift from products to outcomes, their existing models will become liabilities.

They are very asset-intensive and hierarchically organized. They are, by default, independently minded proprietors of their machinery and production assets for which they need complex managerial arrangements in place. Their supply chains focus on the efficient movement of physical goods. They are typically linear and often siloed. Usually being legacy businesses, they are not good at setting up flexible ecosystem relationships.

Start-ups with flat outward-looking management hierarchies and fewer business assets find this much easier. We can therefore expect new digital entrants to increasingly disrupt established structures and relationships. Consider, by looking at Figure 2.4, the many ways the logistics industry is attacked by nimble start-up contenders.

Figure 2.4 – Start-ups Unbundling FedEx, UPS and the Logistics Industry[12]

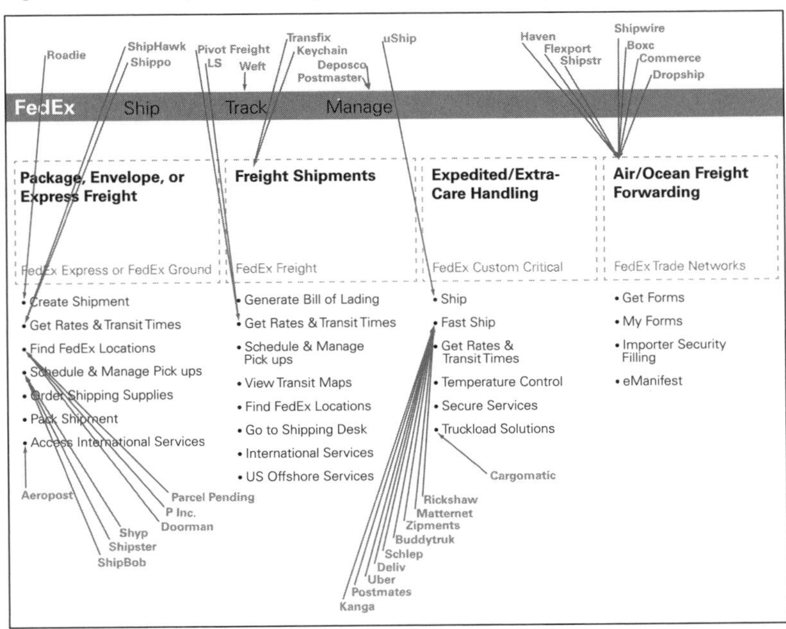

A prominent warning sign is the increasing competition between tech companies such as Google, Apple or even Uber and traditional carmakers. As cars become merely delivery points for lucrative high-margin services, there is a real risk that car manufacturers will end up the junior partners, hardware providers for the tech elite's more valued software.

All this clearly indicates that to compete effectively, incumbent companies need to start thinking about how they will fit into new ecosystems now. The IIoT market is still in its early stage. There is time to adapt, but there will be less and less as the change accelerates.

New Risks and Rewards

As we have seen, the definition and future reality of the Outcome Economy is much more complex than today´s business practices and structures.

It's not just that we are heading into a world where customers demand specified results rather than the bare tools to achieve things themselves. As our ecosystem discussion makes clear, the Outcome Economy will also involve complex networks of companies, sectors, customers and suppliers. This will create various highly nuanced relationships, roles and new business entities. The boundaries within and between businesses will become extremely blurred.

This makes the Outcome Economy a macro-economic concept and a socio-political topic. For instance, to work well and live up to its enormous economic potential it needs a specific regulatory framework – for the unhindered movement of data, intellectual property protection, the cross-border tax treatment of new and complex entities, and liability and warranty rights. These needs are certainly not the focus of this book, but they illustrate the revolutionary and complex ramifications of doing business outcome-based and at a broad level.

Companies will need more and better data to calculate costs, manage risks and track all the factors required to deliver the promised value. New financial instruments and forms of insurance will emerge to manage the risks associated with guaranteeing outcomes. Pricing practices will change, as it becomes possible to model the probability of delivering outcomes. The greater than ever connectedness and cooperation among businesses in new market ecosystems will itself call for new technology platforms.

But the Outcome Economy will also mean that the economic risk of under-utilized assets shifts from the user to the producer. Remember that the power drill for creating a hole in the wall will no longer be owned by the customer but the provider of this specific outcome. This also means that cash flows will change significantly. Producers will receive their remuneration after the outcome has been achieved and not during a preliminary investment phase before usage of an asset.

There will be a number of possible lead and supporting roles: platform owner, data supplier, service aggregator. Many factors will influence these choices, including a business's existing market positions, IT capabilities, risk tolerance and internal cultures.

In sum, the enormous complexity points clearly to the need for a clear, incremental strategy for digitization, in preparation for the Outcome Economy. I will look at how one begins to devise such a strategy in the next chapter.

First, let's take a structured look at the developmental process with which your strategy will need to align.

The Four Future Stages of Industry

How will the journey towards and beyond a fully developed Outcome Economy look? And where do most enterprises in which sectors stand today on this path?

Recent research has identified four principal stages of this journey. In general, the first two phases are incremental by nature and are happening as we speak, whereas phases three and four are both transformational and expected to acquire momentum and mainstream adoption around three to five years down the line.

Stage 1: Operational Efficiency

This is a phase in which, from shop floors in typical manufacturing plants to top-floor executive suites, embedded software enables the connected and intelligent applications, machines, products and people that sustain a more operationally efficient enterprise.

Such digitally automated manufacturing alone can boost productivity by as much as 30 percent. It is already wide practice in the mining industry, for instance: connected site equipment identifies degradation of machinery such as iron ore trucks or train carriages and predicts necessary maintenance. In this sector, such predictive maintenance not only minimizes downtime by as much as 70 percent, it can also reduce overall maintenance costs by up to 30 percent.[14]

Most enterprises active in industrial manufacturing are around halfway through this phase, which is defined by *operational efficiency*. Research shows that around 40 percent of US companies consider their industries to be digital leaders, whereas in Germany and France not even 20 percent believe that. In Asia only 7 percent of Japanese firms see themselves as digitally leading, whereas in China the share reaches already 33 percent.[15]

Figure 2.5 – Evolution Path of the Industrial Internet[13]

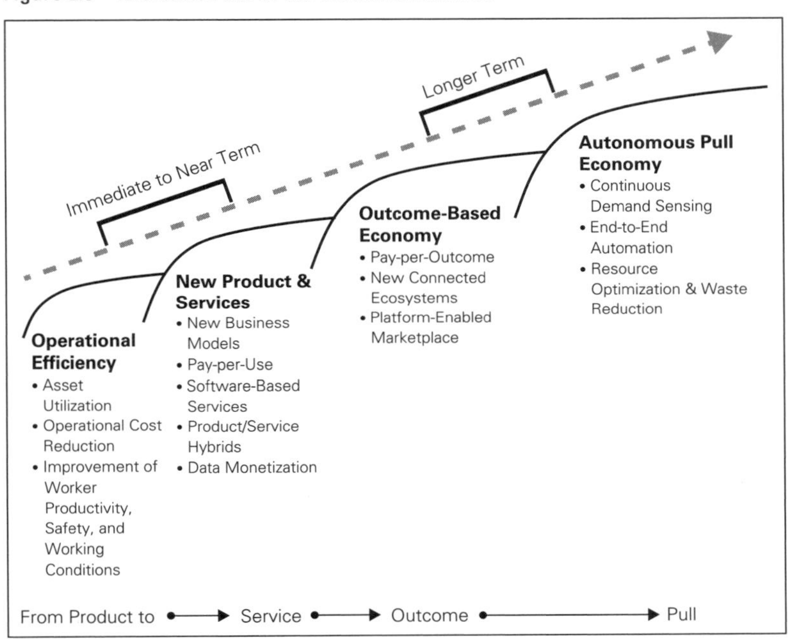

Operational efficiency also covers the optimization of business operations through connectivity. This allows companies to create more customer touchpoints, thus driving revenues.

In this phase, the supply chain will become more flexible, allowing for on-demand customization and real-time access to information. Digital manufacturing will affect the product design process, its lifecycle becoming shorter as technology enables quicker modification.

Production of goods will happen closer to consumption. Service delivery, on the other hand, will drift further from consumption as services can be delivered remotely.

German industrial engineering specialist Siemens, for example, is providing utility companies with advanced smart grid solutions, services focused on data management, and systems integration that will improve their energy efficiency and grid reliability.[16]

Stage 2: New Products and Services

In phase two, new products and services will appear in large numbers, propelled by cloud computing and the broad diffusion of analytics On the basis of wired-up, operationally efficient manufacturing processes, businesses will look further downstream to their final markets. They will find a clientele, either consumers or other businesses, with substantial appetite for intelligent products that can offer added services and value via embedded software.

This will be a decisive step as built-in software provides the foundation for the entirely new hardware functionalities that can fuel innovation and faster time to market. In the most prominent real-life example, the embedding of a whole ecosystem of apps into Apple's iPhone has revolutionized the smartphone and transformed it into the ultimate user interface for mass-consumers' day-to-day life. It has thus kick-started a completely new market. This process will also break into other sectors once the outcome economy has taken off.

For now, real life examples are still sporadic and have the quality of pilots rather than being full-scale. The trend, though, will accelerate in the coming years. US heavy equipment manufacturer Caterpillar, for instance, is already using telematics to enable advanced connected equipment services for its industry segments and their customers.[17] In a similar vein, leading healthcare companies are leveraging a network of connected devices, often coupled with the insights enabled by big data and analytics, to improve patient care. Or take industrial equipment manufacturer Schneider Electric, which is embedding analytics and connectivity into its products and launching new digital products.[18]

Automotive manufacturers can leverage the power of embedded software to build new business models by providing service add-ons giving all sorts of assistance to the driver, bundling information services as subscription services, and treating these hybrids as input for R&D activities.

The user-interface in a GPS receiver that lets car drivers use navigational software in real time is one example of how embedded software can generate new value in this sector. Data flowing back from cars in use can provide input for new car features. The car will increasingly be turned into a platform on wheels, one that will connect more and more with other platforms such as the IT infrastructure for cities or homes. In fact, your car will become a natural extension of your home or your office environment.

Half the value of a vehicle will here already come from software and electronics. But car manufacturers could go much further. By enabling drivers to order in-car entertainment systems and other embedded services directly from their vehicle, for example, they could build much closer and more loyal relationships with them – and open a new sales channel.

Stage 3: The Broad Introduction of Outcomes

At stage three the Outcome Economy will be fully established. The wholly connected, intelligent and smartened-up enterprise, manufacturing connected products with major service elements attached, will be perceptive enough to sense its own needs and those of its customers. This is the phase where connected products will be replaced by connected product systems.

In fact the product will then have grown from a mere hardware item to a smart item, to one that can serve as a platform, to one that can be engulfed with services around it, to one that is hyper-personalized offering entirely new qualities of user experience.

In protracted feedback loops of data-based information, this stage will command enough intuition to relate to the outcomes that enterprises and customers seek. This is the stage when manufacturing will be, to a large extent, put on autopilot and the role of blue-collar and, to an even greater extent, white-collar work will be significantly diminished. It will be an economy where a pay-per-outcome business model will definitively have crowded out most legacy enterprise approaches.

This stage will also be marked by the removal of the final barriers and silos in enterprise processes. By embedding software in production machinery as well as products, meaningful and flexible business ecosystems can be built that will be able to share risk and create integrated, cross-industry product and service bundles that deliver complex and tailored outcomes.

This will also be the moment when sector platforms will have found a meaningful shape and weight and even platforms of platforms will have emerged.

The trend towards individualization of products and services will be fully pronounced, with hyper-tailored offerings that are immediate, highly demand-driven, context-specific and consumed as a service.

Business processes will become much more dynamic and machine-driven at this stage, propelling the need for vastly different services, and skills to support them. Today´s processes are task-oriented, repetitive, sequential and largely driven, supervised and evaluated by humans. In a fully developed Outcome Economy, dynamic machine-defined processes will be driven by artificial intelligence.

What sounds like sci-fi is, to some extent, already workable reality. Consider, for example, Dutch healthcare technology giant Philips and Australian bioinformatics specialist Emotiv. Together they have prototyped a wearable, digitally enabled device that gives muscular dystrophy sufferers control of light switches and temperature thermostats using their own brainwaves. This is a truly cutting-edge application of embedded software.[19] It could have mass-market status in a few years when the Outcome Economy is fully-fledged.

Stage 4: Fully Automated Industry

There is a fourth stage beyond the arrival of the Outcome Economy. This will be focused on further deepening and detailing of digitally orchestrated smart manufacturing processes. It will be marked by autonomous control and full automation from end-to-end. This will mark the full establishment of the IIoT across most industry sectors in the developed world.

Human involvement will be minimized in a system equipped, thanks to embedded software, with a real-time supply chain. Automation, which is also heavily software-steered, will take care of such critical issues as removing skills shortages and providing safety in the manufacture of cars and industrial equipment.

This stage will also see the emergence of the Pull Economy in which products are only assembled when an order is placed. In that regard it will be a phase in which waste production and energy use are enormously reduced and, hence, resources are optimized.

For most players, such fully automated manufacturing processes are a long way off. Many, however, have already embarked on the IIoT journey – and growing numbers recognize that embedded software is key to unlocking its value. Indeed, embedded software is changing not only perceptions of what industrial products and services actually are, but also how they are developed. By connecting devices continuously and in real-time, and enabling new functionalities, it provides the foundation of all that the IIoT promises to deliver.

Takeaways

1. The Industrial Internet of Things (IIoT) will drastically change the way companies work internally, work with each other, and sell to customers.
2. This will lead to "the end of the product" and the rise of a new kind of economy, the Outcome Economy (or "usage economy"). In this new world, tried-and-tested industrial hardware products are not only eclipsed by their much more profitable service qualities, the user experience and the ecosystems they operate in: They are also commerzialized on a per outcome basis. It is the combination of living products and as-a-service business model that make the outcome economy.
3. This will be the era in which industrial companies move away from rigid business silos to more agile ecosystems and alliances with surprising partners. It they don't, they won't survive in the long run.

Chapter 3

03

Digital Super Value – A Guiding Light for Digital Strategy

Manufacturing businesses can reap huge financial rewards from digitizing their whole value chain. As a welcome side effect, society will massively benefit via the external value spread of enterprises. Often, societal gains from digital business strategies are even greater than the gains in EBITDA and sales within enterprises. For business, the value, so to speak, of looking at value is that it is critical in devising a digitization strategy. Different values accrue from digitizing at different speeds (and faster is by no means necessarily better) and different functions in different sectors contain digital value pools of widely varying depth.

Before I go on to look at the practicalities of digitizing existing operations, let's examine the question of value in greater detail. This is not a matter of just getting excited about the next big thing. There are two very good practical reasons for looking at value. First, it will be vital in helping executives make the business case to their organizations. Second, even more compellingly, a granular understanding of *how* digitization drives value creation is, as I will show, vital in devising implementation strategies.

It becomes clear that it is not simply a matter of "To digitize or not to digitize?" Businesses should definitely digitize. But, as I will show, different sectors have different opportunities, with certain functions offering greater value than others. Furthermore, there is the question of the pace at which to digitize in such a rapidly changing landscape.

Figure 3.1 – Digitization in Various Sectors – the Capabilities and Benefits[1]

Sector	Connected Products/Digital Services	Business Outcomes
Connected Health	Monitoring and Treating Illness	Up to 20% Reduction in Disease Burden
	Improving Wellness	$80-600 per Year in Wellness Benefits per User
Connected Home	Core Automation	17% Time Saved from Relevant Activities
	Energy Management – Home	20% Energy Savings
	Safety and Security	10% Reduction in Property Damage Incidents
Connected Office	Human Productivity – Activity Monitoring	5% Productivity Improvement
	Human Productivity – Augmented Reality	10% Productivity Improvement
	Energy Monitoring – Offices	20% Savings
Connected Factory	Operations Optimization	5-12.5% Cost Reduction
	Predictive Maintenance	10-40% Cost Savings
	Inventory Optimization	20-50% Cost Reduction
	Health and Safety	10-25% Savings
Connected Operations	Operations Optimization	5-10% Increase in Worksite Productivity, 10-20% of Consumables, 10-20% of Personnel
	Improved Equipment Maintenance	3-5% Productivity Gain, 5-10% of Equipment Costs, 5-10% of Equipment Maintenance
	Health and Safety Management	10-20% Decrease in Health and Safety Costs
Connected Transport	Safety and Security – Personal Transportation	25% Improvement
	Passenger Vehicles Maintenance/Replacement	10-40% Reduction in Maintenance and 3-5% Longer Vehicle Life
	Aerospace Equipment and Maintenance	10-40% Reduction in Maintenance, 25% Fewer Delays, 3-5% Longer Aircraft Life
Connected City	Air and Water Monitoring	15% Reduction
	Adaptive Traffic Management	10-15% Less Time in Traffic, 10% Reduction in Congestion from Smart Parking
	Autonomous Vehicles (Fully and Partially)	~40% Accident Reduction, 10-15% Fuel/CO_2 Savings
	Resource/Infrastructure Management	35% Fewer Electric Outages, 50% Reduction in Water Leaks, 10% Reduction in Theft

As should already be fairly clear from Chapter 1, the change that is happening now around digital in manufacturing is about a dramatic shift of emphasis: the technology is moving from a sort of sidekick role as the creator of marginal efficiency to become the central, mighty enabler of fundamental innovation, disruption and value. Executives in most manufacturing industries are beginning to understand this.

The value levers are monumental. Where it took Fortune 500 companies an average of 20 years to arrive at individual valuations of a billion dollars,[2] today's digitally driven start-ups can earn their "unicorn" status in just four years. This essentially means that digital technology is driving overall business values on average five times faster than many waves of conventional technological innovation did in the past. What's more, compared to start-ups, the potential gains of digitally transforming existing larger corporations are exponentially greater.

With large companies, however, the old problem arises of getting the Titanic to change course. There are massive infrastructural and cultural change to be made, numerous stakeholders to be kept on board, competing budgetary considerations and the list goes on.

All this should be seen in the light of disintegrating profitability. Industrial equipment manufacturers have reached low single-digit returns on equity, and, while carmakers (at least some) still realize high single digits, both return rates are insufficient to fund the transition to new digitally based business models. In other words the core is too weak to support the move to the New.

There are also, crucially, the risks associated with new technology adoption, especially at scale: legacy non-digital infrastructure may be performing well and one could lose out from replacing it with something untested; the new tech may become obsolete too quickly or prove inefficient, even faulty. But if one waits for competitors to "test" new approaches first, what if those approaches work and put the competitors ahead of you?

Executives find themselves torn between these troubling potential outcomes. As I will show, examining value is vital in pointing a way through this bewildering and potentially maddening conflict.

As I indicated in Chapter 2 and will elucidate further in this chapter, it is right to be cautious and incremental in implementing digital. In fact, the headline of the journey from old to the New is the concept of the "wise pivot," a programmatic journey of change mapped out below.

To transition to digital, a business should grow its core and use the proceeds to invest more and more in the New as Figure 3.2 illustrates.

Figure 3.2 – The Four Overlapping Steps of the Wise Pivot[3]

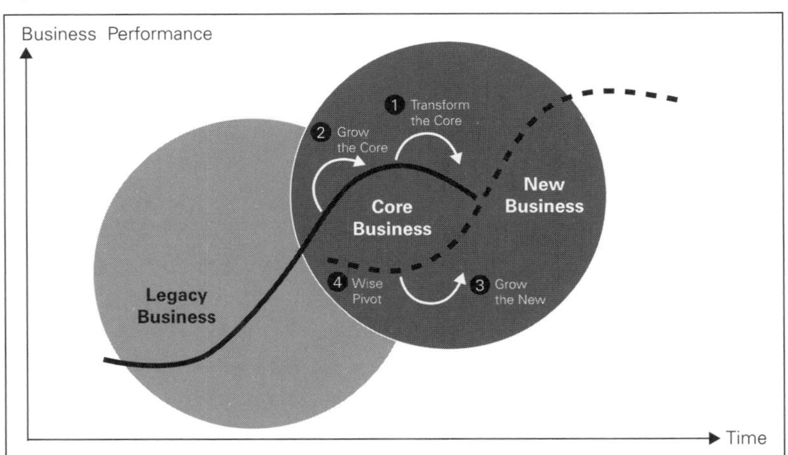

As I will go on to show, such an approach is of fundamental importance. However, as I will also show, there is a difference between adapting in a way that is simply ad hoc and opportunist and doing so according to a strategy based on real underlying needs and opportunities and that positions a company to take fuller and fuller advantage of digital as matters progress.

Two Speeds Create Massive Value Deposits

One can understand just how much value there is to be gained from digitization and where it lies by looking at the gap between the speed of technological innovation itself and the rate at which businesses are implementing it.

Technology knows no standstill. Sensor technology is constantly pushing towards greater sophistication; telecoms providers are continually introducing new capacity in mobile data transmission; cloud services offer steadily more tailored backbones for businesses; ever more powerful analytics software is coming of age, morphing into routine tools for the shop floor.

The trajectory and pace of this intellectual work is entirely uncorrelated to the rollout momentum of the enterprises intended to put it into use. Although unmanned digitized speed factories – industrial plants, automatically responding to order sizes of just ten pairs of sports shoes in magenta crimson, say – are now clearly profitable business cases, this radical technological enterprise set-up is a long way from being deployed overnight in all industries that could benefit.

As I have indicated, this is because, as difficult as it is to create world-beating innovations, further difficulties arise when putting them into practice in the proving ground of business implementation. There is therefore a certain inevitability about technology always looking at business in the rearview mirror. But it is in the gap between the two that one finds the potential value that will guide implementation

As digital technology's progress has become inordinately fast, a value deposit of gigantic proportions has built for society and enterprises to tap. If industrial manufacturing sectors adopt digital technology at, say, a third of the rapidity with which digital technology becomes available, the potential value for business becomes huge.

Recent studies on individual value deposits in various industries have put a figure on them.

An overall calculus, based on detailed screening of various sectors, arrived at $100tn of value globally that is ready to be released by applying digital technology to businesses of all kinds through to 2025.[4]

This striking figure breaks down in a very intriguing way: a fifth of that buried value sleeps untouched in just four sectors: automotive, consumer goods, energy and logistics.

So, for instance, digital transformation could boost power generating businesses' operating profits by nearly 50 percent, whereas in the automotive sector where much of the low-hanging fruit of digital value benefits have already been harvested, one would still expect a positive EBIT-push of around 10 percent over the next decade.[5]

The Societal Benefits

Digital technologies are indeed creating deep and verifiable profit pools for manufacturing and service enterprises and their various internal functions. As a welcome side effect, this also creates significant external benefits for society overall. In fact, strikingly, the value gains for the public outside of companies often actually surpass the value created for the respective industry sectors.

There is, for example, a huge societal issue in that mankind simply cannot absorb the increases in numbers of people and their expectations from life. Just look at travel. Whether by air, train or car-based in cities – it simply won't continue to work using the current frameworks. Instead, societies need to use assets such as roads and railways much more efficiently. Improved efficiency of asset use is a key result of industrial digitization, carrying with it huge societal benefits.

Figure 3.3 – Trapped Value for Industry and Society over the Next Decade[6]

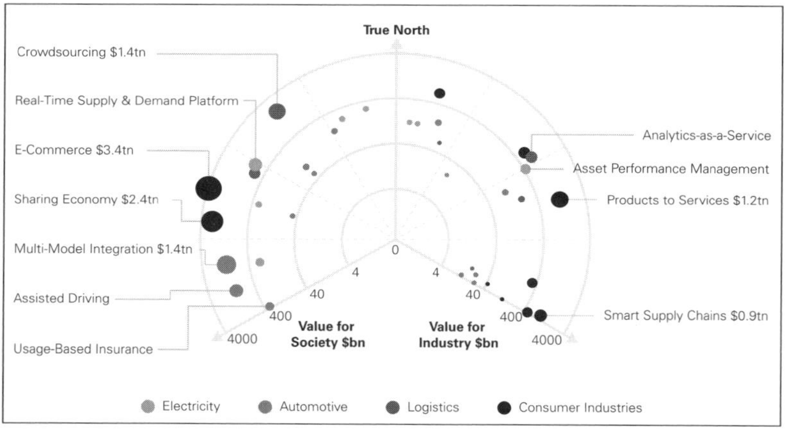

Business examples can be grouped into cases where value-creation for society and enterprise is equally high and cases where it is strongly biased towards one or the other. Over time, this can change. Cases in which value for society is low at the beginning can become higher later and vice versa. There are cases such as the autonomous car where the societal value is very high from the beginning – in terms of massively reduced road deaths – and of almost no immediate value for car manufacturers, though they may find value there later.

Figure 3.4 – Value Case for Autonomous Car[7]

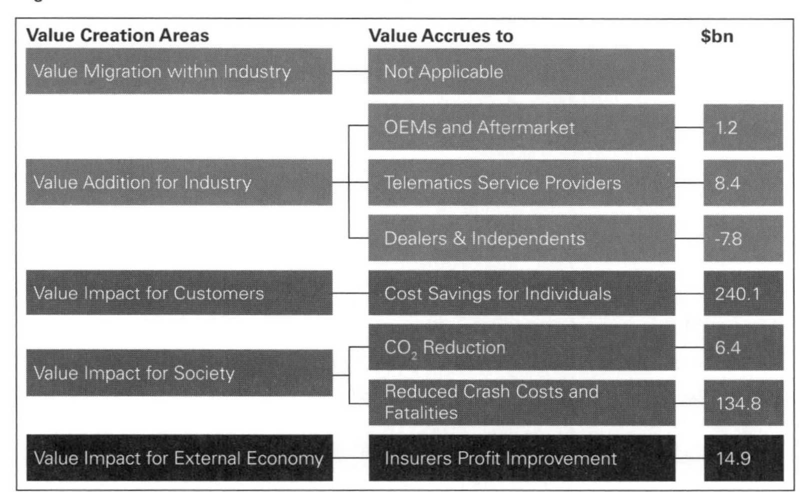

Individual examples of societal benefits are plentiful and, analyzing them, it becomes clear that digital technology can in fact part-resolve the most urgent problems facing the world today.

Energy

Take energy usage. Emissions from energy producers have roughly doubled over the last three decades to unsustainable levels. According to our calculation, the electricity-generating sector alone could unlock value from digital transformation of more than $1.3tn, creating a further $1.7tn for society from 2016 through to 2025 in the wake.[8]

You and I – the general public – could, for instance, benefit as energy customers through the deployment of smart meters, giving us better control over our energy budgets.

By the same token, carbon emissions will be reduced through a much more decentralized and flexible digital micro-management of energy generation and consumption.

Put all the effects together and you arrive at just over $2tn in benefit to society over the next decade.[9]

Logistics

The logistics sector harbors substantial potential benefits from digitization for the public. Our calculations show that these stand at $2.4tn – actually far outstripping the energy sector's potential value gains.[10]

Retail and wholesale transport and delivery services create 13 percent of all global climate-damaging emissions. Digital technology can reduce these emissions by up to 11 percent over the next ten years. And by shrinking emissions in the long-term by up to 90 percent and realizing cost benefits of around a quarter in last-mile deliveries, digital drone technology could soon grow into a mighty value generator for society in the logistics industry.[11]

The main value contributions in logistics, however, will come from digitally fine-tuned transport fleets, from van, warehouse and hub infrastructure, and from transport, with digital cab services such as Uber becoming part of the logistics ecosystem.

Finally, as in the energy sector, digitizing logistics promises huge value creation for individual households. Real-time tracking systems and delivery rates, driven down by increased digital competition in a much more transparent market, create value for us all to the tune of around $800bn over the coming decade.[12]

Insurance

To show that society can reap rewards from digitization in many forms, let's look at one more subject of our studies: usage-based car insurance, where on-board units record driver behavior. Parameters such as overall miles per month, speed acceleration, lane changing and brake patterns are transmitted to the insurer, which applies intelligent algorithms to issue a highly individualized monthly insurance policy, reflecting the "danger" the policy holder poses.

This is a great example of how digital allows physical hardware and cleverly designed services to be combined to an unprecedented product profile with enormous societal benefits. A recent value-at-stake analysis estimates that this form of car insurance would change driving behavior and thus could save more than 150,000 lives by 2025. What's more, accurately priced insurance also means lower costs for consumers and reduced crash and repair costs for all other stakeholders.[13]

All the examples given show the truth of eminent Harvard Business School scholar Clayton Christensen's well-known hypothesis that the public gains more from digitizing established industries than from disruptive digital start-ups. In short, incumbents win over challengers here. The sheer scale of established industries makes them by far the biggest benefactors to society once they digitize their processes and functions. But that, of course, depends on them actually getting their digital makeovers underway.

What's in it for Business?

Now, what about value gains for enterprises – digital technology's measurable effects on performance figures such as EBITDA, sales, the balance sheet and profits and loss accounts?

In the following sections I will guide you through Accenture's recent study on this, focusing on one sector example, but also providing the key figures for all the sectors the study looked at. In the end, as you will see, these observations will reveal some key guidelines for manufacturing sectors generally.

The study looked at four sectors. Two were among the ones I said above had the greatest potential to reap value from digitization: automotive and consumer packaged goods. It also looked at pharmaceuticals and industrial engineering, where, as you will see, there are also significant wins to be made. After all, no sector can afford to be complacent here.

The study looked at what these sectors can do in the short term – that is, over the next three years. The aims were to see which of their functions contained the most "trapped value," and also assess the relative values of digitizing at different paces.

Regarding the latter aim, we looked at four different scenarios:

1. What happens when a sector pursues business as usual with no digitizing initiatives?

2. What happens when the sector's value chain is part-digitized on an opportunistic and ad hoc basis?

3. What happens when the sector shifts incrementally but systematically across its existing business?

4. What happens when the sector makes a wholesale shift to digital business models enabled by new digital products and services?

We can dispense with scenarios (1) and (2) above immediately. Carrying on with business as usual – either not digitizing or adopt-

Figure 3.5 – Four Digital Transformation Scenarios[14]

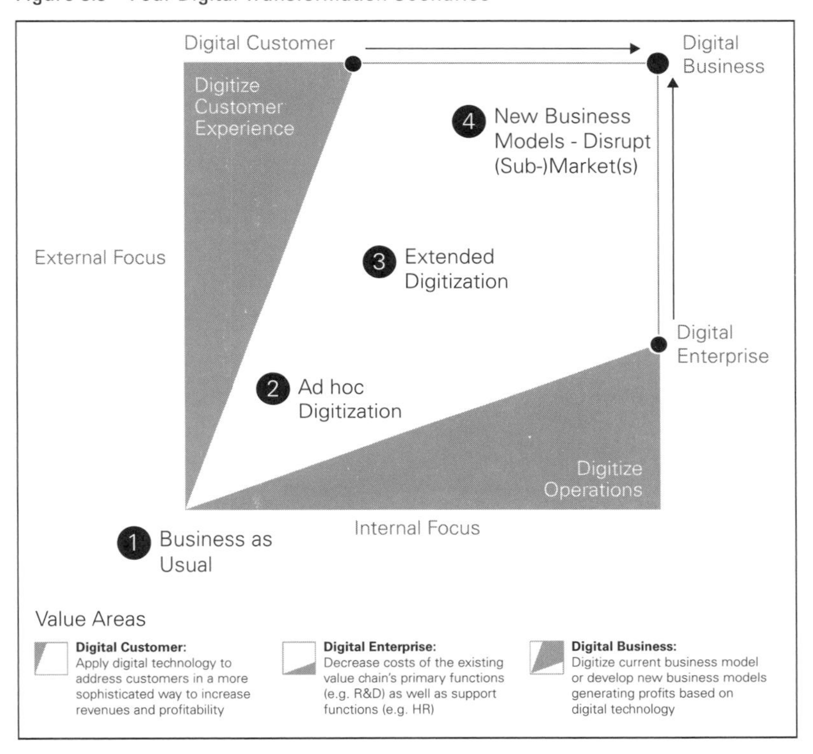

ing digital technology only here and there without any overall strategy – will incur drastic negative effects on profits and sales.

In our simulation for the automotive sector, for instance, we let a $50bn turnover car producer stick to what it has. The result is what one would expect. The enterprise would quickly feel the heat from competitors that have at least part-digitized. Market share would be lost to rivals and a growing innovation gap would open. In addition, the shareholder value would deteriorate and cost structures become uncompetitive. The company would suffer an overall 15.6 percent fall in EBITDA profits – or a $780m shrinkage in absolute terms.[15]

Similar simulations in other sectors showed similar results. For instance, an industrial engineering firm would lose $280m on a turnover of $10bn, whereas a provider of construction equipment would have $495m less on a sales base of $20bn.[16]

Automotive – the Vanguard Efficiency Seekers

The automotive sector is a good one to look at here because it has been such an early adopter of automation and digital technologies such as CAD and EDI across engineering and manufacturing, just to cite a few examples. It implemented numerically controlled production robots as early as the 1970s, for huge efficiency gains, and has accrued further huge value gains ever since by updating both manufacturing and business technology in wave after wave of innovation.

Figure 3.6 – Digital Value Realization in Automotive[17]

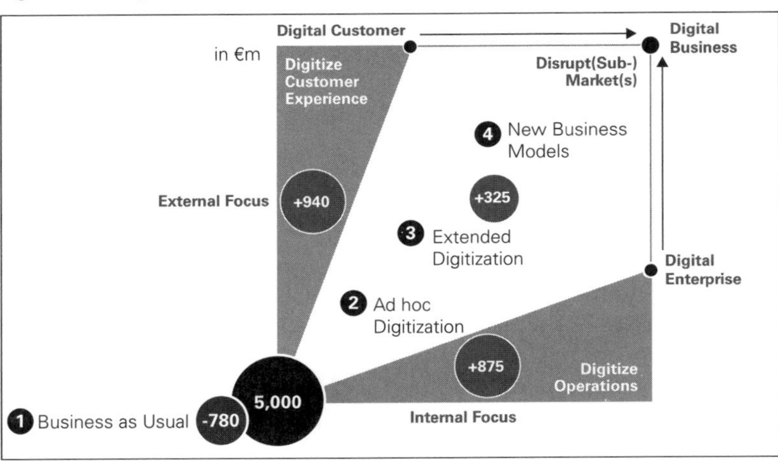

Nevertheless, as you will see, this industry's trapped value unlockable by digital remains substantial. This is particularly so given that the sector is about to dramatically change its operating mode again, with the car becoming a piece of hardware and a platform for services within broader ecosystems.

Short-term trends in the sector clearly indicate the challenges around digital, but also show how inevitable digitization is, due to the value it adds and the related trends in the surrounding ecosystem. I expect the automotive industry to face the following six dominating trends over the next five years:

1. The more the car's internal workings become dependent on digital algorithms, the more time discrepancies will arise between development cycles for hardware and software. This phenomenon is common in other industries and is not easy to manage.

2. Climate change will force car manufacturers to research engine technology running at ever-lower emission levels. This is simply impossible without ultra-precise steering software for ignition and other parts of a motor. Digital components and software will therefore soon be indispensable.

3. The car will leave behind its functional set-up as a pure means of transport. The future is the connected car. A vehicle will be hardware with suites of regularly updated, fast-paced software on board. This means that just to survive, car producers will have to be able to deal with advanced data analytics and, latterly, handle huge amounts of privacy-sensitive customer data safely.

4. The car will leave behind its status as a disconnected means of transport for lone individuals. Digital car and ride-sharing schemes and technologies will be paramount for remaining competitive in the future automotive sector. Cars will soon start to move and act in concert, be managed in fleets and be swallowed up by capillary and highly pervasive mobility concepts.

Digital technology is, of course, not just vital to controlling these complex transport ensembles, it's what makes them possible.

5. In as much as it remains a consumer product, the car will finally succumb to the same fragile loyalty other consumer products experience in the era of hyper-connected consumers, constantly tempted by new features elsewhere and influenced by crowd-sourced word of mouth. Car brands will have to craft offline and online experiences into customer journeys that work harder to maintain loyalty.

Based on this, our assessment is that car manufacturers going down the digitization route, working towards a complete digital operating model, will globally increase their turnover by 15.6 percent or $216bn in the four years to 2020.

The margin push digital technology brings about is also quite impressive. We calculated that the overall EBITDA for car companies – the earnings before interest payment, taxes, depreciation and amortization – would collectively grow by 42.8 percent or $59bn.

By 2020, the major potential derived from digitization of the customer experience and internal operations in the existing value chain will be exploited (Scenario 3). Therefore, the main digital-enabled uplift will be caused by new business models in the subsequent years.

Which Digitization Strategy Creates the Most Value?

To invest in digital technology and do so in a systematic way is clearly logical for automotive. But how should one go about this? Let's look at some numbers for the most advanced new digital business models, for a manufacturer with $50bn annual turnover.[18]

If you implemented a mobility-on-demand approach, business-to-consumer or peer-to-peer car sharing schemes, or even an inter-modal travel platform connecting various transport methods such as trains, planes, buses, bikes and cars, it would earn you, in the underdeveloped markets for these services today, just $260m.[19]

Connected car solutions for vehicle-related services or a platform for open mobility apps, would earn you a miniscule $35m.[20]

Likewise there is no significant demand yet for autonomous driving services, consumer data to be sold at a premium or a living service platform around specific car brands. According to our scenario this would propel your EBITDA result only by another $10m.[21]

Finally, imagine you leapfrogged part-digitization and implemented all the radical new business models for the automotive industry overnight, tonight. The total EBITDA gain over the next four years would not exceed a modest 6 percent or $325m – $20m less than what you would get from just digitizing your support functions in a part-digital approach.[22]

Over all, we found that those focussing on digitizing their internal operations and the customer experience will realize 36.3 percent EBITDA growth – or an absolute total of $1.815bn.[23]

The New IIoT Economy is Becoming a Reality

It's very clear. Up to 2020 the greater value in automotive will be derived from part-digitizing the value chains operating on traditional business models, not going the whole hog. This is partly because old-style legacy infrastructure and processes still offer plenty of potential for value creation and partly because consumer markets are not yet developed enough for the suggested future business models. The fully-fledged digital manufacturing entity with suitable new business and service models should wait for the decade beyond 2020.

All that said, make no mistake: in those years following 2020, the new IIoT-based economy will become a reality with increasing speed. One must prepare for this by creating a nucleus of digital capability that can be built upon. As unwise as it would be to do everything now, it would still not be as unwise as doing nothing or adopting digital ad hoc and without a plan.

The following table shows where automotive manufacturers have already started to go digital.

Figure 3.7 – Existing Industry Players and Cross-Industry Innovators[24]

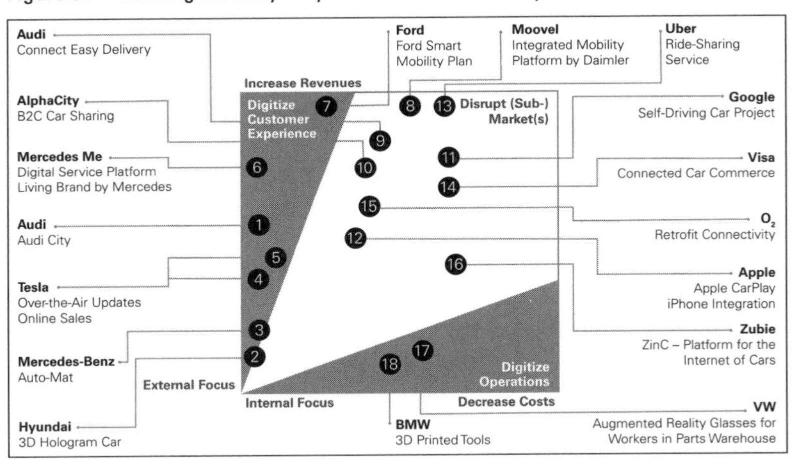

Think in terms of two value chains, core and new. One should invest in both, gradually shifting the emphasis from old to new.

So start digitizing existing value chains and – largely in parallel – begin working on new software-driven business models. Putting the emphasis on the old value chain will deliver the financial means to invest in the business models. Eventually, once the Outcome Economy has taken full shape, you will have the new operational models ready to reap the full rewards.

To further refine the investment strategy, it becomes vital to look at the value of investing in different functions.

Not all Functions are Value-Deep

Assessing the value pools of individual functions within automotive gives a very mixed picture.

For this purpose, as I have indicated, we did a model calculation, using a representative car manufacturer with an assumed annual turnover of $50bn. The results were as follows.

Figure 3.8 – Digitization Levers and Value Potentials[25]

Research & Development $115m		Manufacturing & Supply $415m		Marketing & Sales $715m		Aftersales $225m	
Analytics-Based PLM Improvement	65	Digital Supply Chain Management	125	Predictive & Personalized Offers	235	Predictive Maintenance	30
Virtual Product Development & Prototyping	50	Digital-Enabled Manufacturing	250	Digital-Enabled Lead Management	195	Personalized Aftersales Offers	90
		Asset Efficiency	40	Analytic-Based Media Spend Optimization	100	Digitization of Face-to-Face Experience	10
				Centralized Digital Content Management	100	3D Printing of Spare Parts	5
				POS Digitalization	25 / 5	Over-the-Air Features	25
				Online Sales	55	Digital-Enabled Workforce	30
						Aftersales Online Store	35

Revenue Impact = EBITDA Potential of 13.0% ($650m)
Cost Impact = EBITDA Potential of 23.3% ($1,165m)

Support Functions $345m	
Digital-Enabled HR	10
Digital-Enabled Procurement	75
Digital-Enabled IT	180
Digital-Enabled Finance	80

a) Marketing, Sales and Aftersales

Digitization would deliver the most value to marketing and sales, boosting it by 14.3 percent or over $715m in the part-digitization scenario. Separately, aftersales would bring an additional $225m in the extended digitization scenario (Number 3).[26]

Obviously, this is not core manufacturing capability and it is, perhaps, surprising that it delivers so much value. It becomes less surprising when one considers how many potential areas for innovation there are here: personalized service offers based on predictive analytics, direct online sales, digitization of point of sale, new digital marketing channels, digitally optimized media spend and centralized digital content management on websites and social media platforms. Our analysis showed that our putative car business would benefit short-term from investing in all of these and should do so.

b) R&D, Engineering and Manufacturing

The next deepest value pool was in our car business's core engineering and manufacturing segments.

Better orchestration of supply chains with assembly lines via digital precision steering, selective improvements of the various manufacturing processes on the shop floor, an efficiency boost when it comes to utilization – all these contribute to substantial value gains in manufacturing. Collaborative robots are expected to boost productivity by 71 percent while smart helmets and other augmented reality devices will push productivity by an expected 56 percent.

We estimated, on the basis of our model enterprise's size, that more than $715m in additional EBITDA could be unlocked in manufacturing and a further $115m in engineering, boosting its value overall by around 8.3 percent.

c) Business Support Functions

Interestingly, tasks such as human resources management, IT support, procurement, and finance all profit in their own way from digital technology such as robotics or blockchain. In the car company model assessment we found the value gains to be almost seven percent or $345m.

Our analysis, laid out in Figure 3.9, shows that how functions deliver value from digitization depends on the sector. Industrial equipment manufacturing (IE) finds it in functions such as research and development, manufacturing processes and supply chains, whereas marketing offers only modest potential. Marketing is, on the other hand, deeply promising for the consumer goods sector. The value potential in pharmaceuticals meanwhile is already heavily geared towards new business models.

How to Find the Right Pivots

While the value pools vary from sector to sector, our examination of the four sectors in our study leaves us with three valuable guidelines applicable to all:

Conclusion 1: Don't do business as usual

To return to the sector study we spotlighted, a digitally inactive automotive brand with $50bn revenues risks $780m of its EBITDA and misses profit opportunities of $2.14m through to 2020. The general point is, business as usual should not be pursued as a strategic option for a sustainable and profitable business performance. It equates to losing revenues, market share, EBITDA, competitive strength, and, for listed companies, shareholder value.

Figure 3.9 – Digital Industry X.0 Unlocks many Value Sources Across Various Industries[27]

	Auto OEM	OES	IEE	HCE	CD	CGS	LS
IIoT – New Business Model	15%	12%	36%	15%	21%	25%	60%
Marketing & Sales	33%	3%	7%	24%	29%	30%	15%
Research & Development	6%	19%	9%	6%	5%	5%	5%
Manufacturing & Supply Chain	19%	39%	22%	25%	20%	20%	15%
Aftersales	11%	6%	13%	14%	10%	15%	–
Support Functions	16%	21%	13%	16%	15%	5%	5%
EBITDA Growth (2016-2020)	€430m	€310m	€480m	€780m	€300m	€900m	€2,000m
	42.8%	31.8%	41.6%	78.0%	29.4%	60.0%	67.0%
EBITDA CAGR	7.4%	5.7%	7.2%	12.2%	5.3%	7.0%	8.0%

Conclusion 2: Partial digitization and new digital business models – do both

Taking a first seed investment in new business models is the best way to counter cannibalization effects and to establish the foundations for the next generation of industry-dominant business models. New digital business models and part-digitization do not exclude each other. On the contrary, combining both maximizes future growth potentials in terms of EBITDA and revenues. Again, to return to our automotive example, digitization has the potential to grow EBITDA by $1.8bn (36.3 percent) per $50bn of revenue through partial digitization and an additional $325m (6.5 percent) through new business models.

Conclusion 3: Unlock digitization opportunities with a custom-made digital strategy

Digital champions focus on five key enablers when defining their digital transformation agenda: vision, roadmap, traction, team and decisions. Effective digital strategies should be tailored to the distinct characteristics of an organization and leverage its strengths to capture digital opportunities and manage risks. The different strategic options and corresponding EBITDA potentials have to be evaluated for the brand in detail, via an individual cost-benefit analysis.

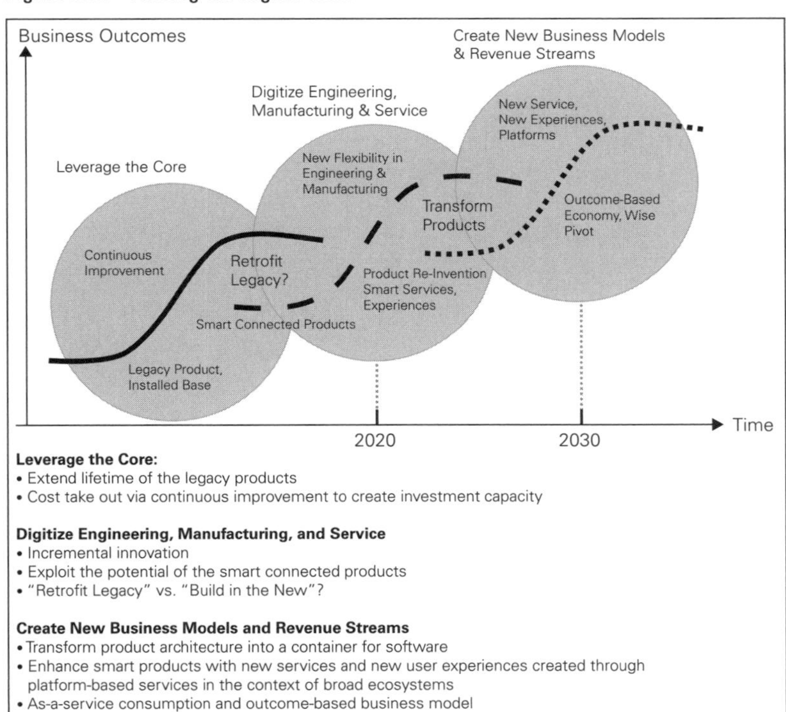

Figure 3.10 – Finding the Right Pivots[28]

If we step back from the very detailed number crunching for different sectors, we see the bigger picture of how a clever digitization strategy implemented at the right time can make a difference. It all comes down to finding the right pivots at the core of your business. To strengthen them digitally will give you the financial power to find even more operational efficiency and get your innovation engine running. This in turn will eventually provide the budgets for thinking up and realizing new business models and revenue streams based on connected products and services. As the graphic below indicates, it is a matter of working through various S-curves at the right time.

Takeaways

1. Business as usual is over. Manufacturing companies can reap huge immediate and future financial rewards from digitizing their whole value chain. Society as a whole will also massively benefit via enterprises' external value spread.
2. Understanding value is critical for an industrial business in devising a digitization strategy. Different values accrue from digitizing at different speeds. Different functions in different industrial sectors contain digital value pools of widely varying depth.
3. Although new digital business models have yet to deliver on their promise, only those companies investing ahead of existing and emerging competitors will capture the potential and establish leadership.

PART II

How to Make the Most of the Digital Industrial Transformation

Chapter 4

Six "No-Regret" Capabilities – the Journey Towards Digital, Mapped out Simply

Although digitally transforming an enterprise looks at first like a scary root-and-branch upheaval of all functions, there are six core capabilities executives can focus on when taking the first steps towards a full-blown IIoT-powered enterprise. These are investments that, from the first day of implementation, will pay off. To gradually filter them into an up-and-running business is easier than is commonly thought. This is the beauty of a digital business: one can start at minimal entry-levels and scale if appropriate. In this approach experimentation or even outright failure is encouraged. A path explored and terminated appropriately rules out options, while also providing information about the potential success of others. This is a key characteristic of the agile, digital world, contrasting starkly with historic business development approaches.

If you have not yet started to digitize your business, the first steps probably feel like entering a jungle of complexity without map, compass or GPS, and a discouraging number of tasks and imperatives laid out before you. The spectrum of critical points at which the organization has to be moved forward looks enormous, while the interdependencies of functions seem mindboggling and the risks huge. Even if they see the advantages themselves, business leaders can therefore struggle to spell them out to shareholders and wider stakeholders.

From Old World to New World on Many Different Paths

Let's start by reminding ourselves of the destination points. Businesses now largely based on non-coordinated manually activated functions and procedures will eventually be controlled by extensive self-organization and autonomous software intelligence. They will, over time, transition from centrally steered, part-automated production processes with managers approaching markets via old-school anticipative analysis, to an economy where processes mostly respond automatically to external data impulses in real-time – from sources such as connected products in the field, suppliers and social media.

For this admittedly epic voyage to go smoothly, a lot does indeed have to change on the ground in real-life businesses. The sites, machines and equipment, workforce, materials and component supply chains, business processes, product platforms, facilities, and environmental parameters – everything appears to need to be advanced in close alignment.

One could draw an "old world to new world" road map, giving a cinemascope view (Figure 4.1).

Figure 4.1 – Old World to New World Road Map[1]

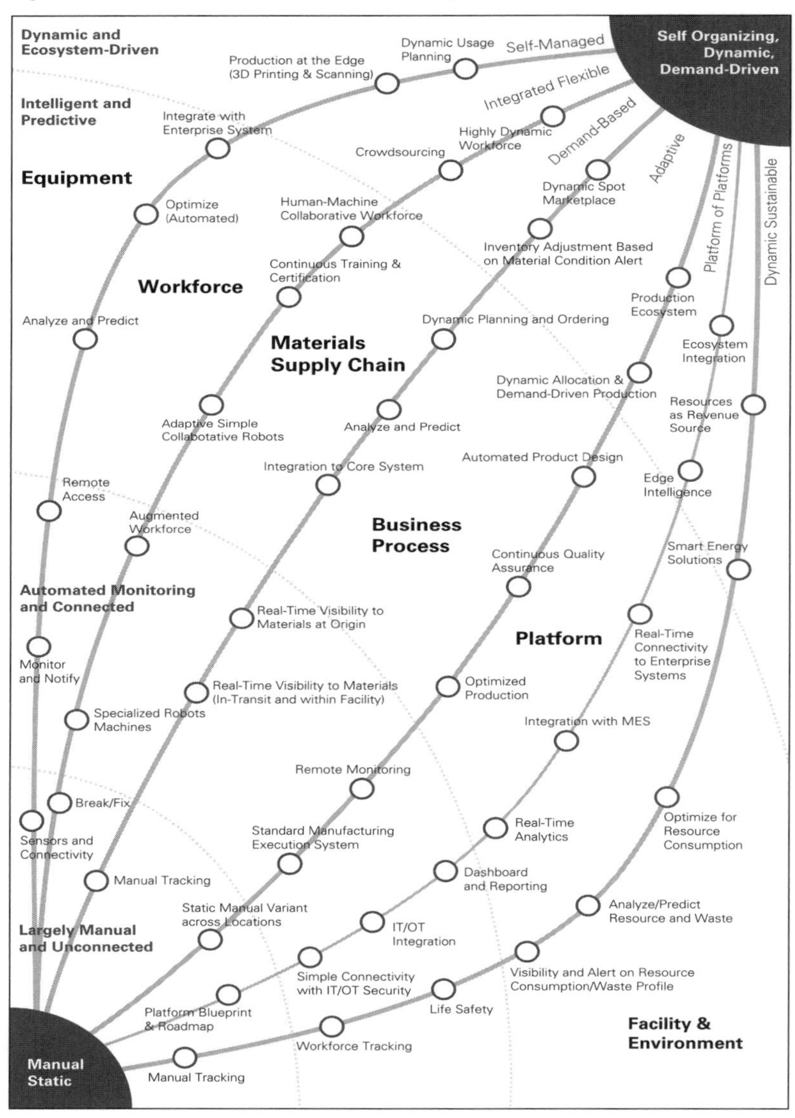

I estimate that most of today's businesses, especially in the industrial manufacturing sector, have just passed phase one and entered

phase two, where things have begun to be automated, monitored and connected in an elementary way (see Figure 4.1). Production processes and the logistics behind them have to a larger or lesser degree already been automated and the workforce sporadically equipped with augmenting technology.

In this phase, most companies' supply chains already offer a degree of real-time visibility. Often the most crucial step is being taken: integrating an enterprise's operational technology (the steering technology behind machine parks and equipment) with its information technology (the traditionally separated spine business processes such as ERP).

But only in the next stage on the chart, where the business becomes truly software-intelligent and predictive, will we notch closer to producing outcomes by rolling out innovative bundles of connected products and digital services.

And only in the stage after that, referred to as "dynamic and ecosystem-driven" on the chart, will we be running a business that is fully plugged into a buzzing outcome economy with vast interconnected ecosystems, platform product services, and low-latency, tailored manufacturing processes.

The fourth step will then only be a tiny advance to the Pull Economy where businesses have so much intelligent technology on board that human physical input, as well as managerial planning and execution, is reduced to a minimum and enterprises spring into action on demand signals from markets.

Schneider Electric Digital Service Factory – the Move from Product to Services

Schneider Electric is a leading global industrial equipment manufacturer with around 160,000 staff. The company's goal is to develop connected technologies, solutions and services to manage energy and automation processes in both utilities and industrial manufacturing businesses.

Schneider Electric, turning over around €25bn annually (fiscal year 2016), is keen to look beyond hardware manufacturing to new business lines.

A team of specialists is helping to build the infrastructure and devise the processes of a newly created Digital Service Factory (DSF) within Schneider Electric. This platform provides Schneider Electric on the one hand with analytics capabilities around predictive maintenance, monitoring and energy optimization of its products, the basis for a later stage end-to-end closed data loop feeding into research and development, and other functions.

Figure 4.2 – Providing Digital Innovation as a Service[2]

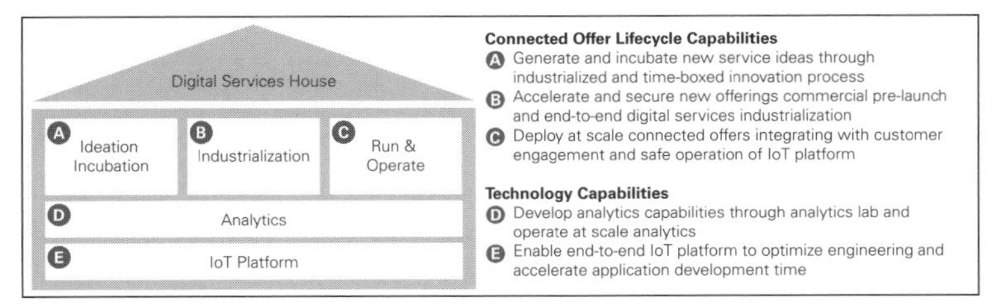

On the other hand, the DSF gives advice on new service designs as well as strategic guidance on how to market and price such new digital services. This will enable the company to leverage millions of connected assets across its infrastructure and customer sites and rapidly build and scale new offerings in areas such as predictive maintenance, asset monitoring, and energy optimization.

Overall the DSF will speed up development at Schneider Electric from ideation to industrialization, including generating and incubating new ideas, designing and testing potential offerings, deploying and scaling offerings, and providing the analytics and IIoT capabilities to accelerate application development time.

Figure 4.3 – From Pilot to Industrialized Service[3]

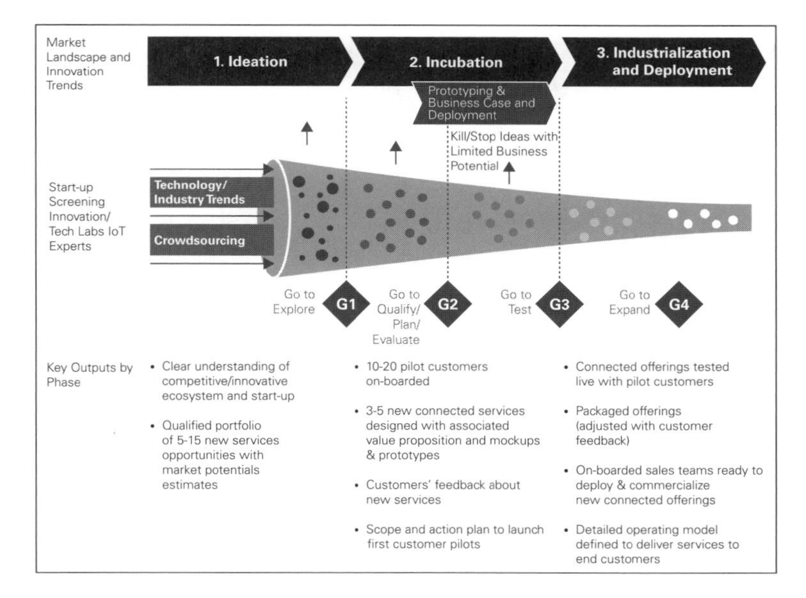

The main goal achieved is to cut the time from product ideation to market testing from three years to less than eight months. The company delivered a three-fold reduction in time to market and has boosted incremental revenues exponentially.

Be Adaptive and Relaxed but Curious and Visionary – and Get Going

If this still sounds overwhelming, fortunately the correct strategy for achieving it is a much less so: it is matter of advancing iteratively, always paying attention to practical results, not forcing a single big revolutionary change. In most companies there is no need to take the huge leap of skipping digital prototyping, testing and piloting, let alone abandoning your core legacy processes if they are still profitable.

This is not just a matter of making things easier and more manageable. In this case, easier really is also more efficient. Why? First, because you are working with untried technologies and processes that must be started small to minimize risk. Second, the landscape is so complex and changeable that there is no pre-defined course through it, especially given that each organization is different.

The charm of building the IIoT, then, is flexibility. Even beyond piloting, it is right for digital to be an incomplete patchwork in your enterprise for quite a while. Start with small digitization projects within clearly defined areas such as R&D, manufacturing or field service, then take what works to other areas and scale up. The point is to create the groundwork for an ever more integrated and automated set of capabilities. Remember that technology is advancing at a rapid and increasing pace, so more help will come in the future from that direction.

It is a matter of behaving a little like a start-up. Rapid experimentation – the rule of "deploy if successful, move on to the next idea, if not" – is standard within these firms. There should ideally be multiple rapid-experimentation sites across your enterprise to get the digital ball rolling.

There is no point though in directionless experimentation *per se*. Your start-up enthusiasm should be channelled down certain clear routes. First, if you devise a digital solution within one of your business units, think strictly along the lines of customer experience. But secondly, also keep an eye on your internal processes, which deserve at least as much experimentation when introducing digital.

Thirdly, you should, of course, also invest a good deal of your experimental energy in new digitally based products and services.

The further good news is, even with this piecemeal approach, digital will add value to your business from the first steps you take.

All this means the pragmatic, improvisational, adaptive leader type is much better suited to the building phase of digitizing enterprises than the narrow-focused technocrat following a clear and rigid blueprint.

Don't worry about either having missed the boat or been overzealous in your digitization process. The key thing is to make a start – and make it now. No business can afford not to digitize. The sooner you start, the sooner you will feel traction in your digital push and, for instance, be able to put up market-entry barriers to potential competitors. Still the overall recommendation is to do this with an open mind: get moving into digital by being as adaptive, relaxed, courageous and visionary as possible and absolutely give yourself plenty of space for trial and error.

Design Thinking Speeds up Service Development Processes

With its roots in product design, Design Thinking is a perfect methodology for finding and developing services around products that customers really want. Desirability for users, technical feasibility and economic viability are a Design Thinking process's main focuses.

At Accenture the methodology comprises six stages: discovery, description, ideation, prototyping, testing, and finally implementation of a service or product design.

Design Thinking is essentially a group process in which everyone involved in using a final product or service is consulted – either through interviews or as a participant in brainstorming, debate and practical work of various kinds. Iteration is key within a Design Thinking process.

A key aim is to break down the silos that usually separate relevant parties. So, for instance, to develop a technical design for a new punch press in the automotive sector, a controller, who thinks in terms of productivity, might speak to engineers, whose views are driven by technical blueprints, and shop floor workers who may be guided more by ergonomic aspects. Discussions and other interactions allow them to find commonalities and ultimately speak with one voice about design needs.

Note that here, the shop floor workers are the end-users. Getting the product or service to work for the people who use it is Design Thinking's ultimate focus. The methodology's simple but surprisingly revolutionary innovation, therefore, is to always include end-users in the design process.

A variety of methods are used for this. Discussion, brainstorming and social media scanning can be extremely productive, but even greater insight can be gained from crowdsourcing or observing users working with existing offerings or new prototypes. The great advantage of this is that people often reveal needs of which they themselves were unaware.

For the design of new digital services, the customer experience is likewise paramount. So a car manufacturer using Design Thinking would bring together drivers with its R&D engineers, marketers, and software experts. Among other techniques, these groups might work to find a "persona," the ideal representative user of the planned car service. Based on this, they can describe user needs in

Figure 4.4 – Design Thinking Methodology[4]

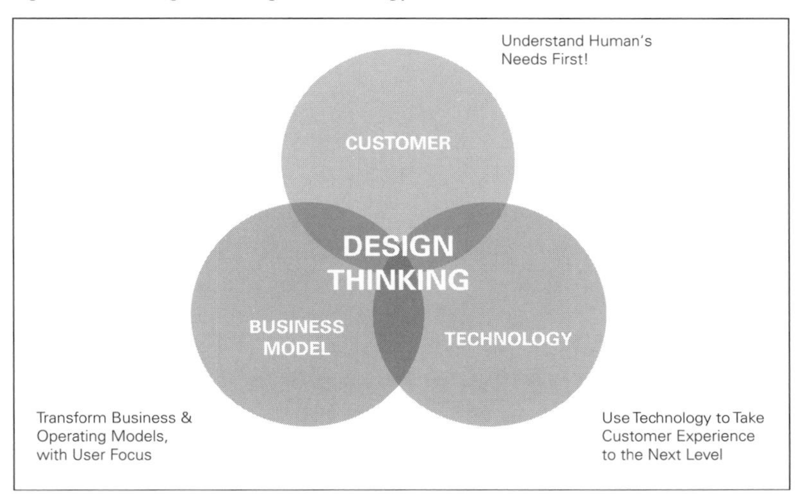

as much detail as possible. Co-Creation is a key element in Design Sprints.

A characteristic benefit of Design Thinking is that results from the numerous discussions, supervised by trained facilitators, are fed back for new filtering into various stages of the process. In that regard, the methodology very much matches what software developers do in their contemporary "agile development" routines.

The big advantage of the highly organized and disciplined Design Thinking approach is that palpable outcomes are conceived much earlier than in conventional development processes. In a typical service creation exercise with 25 people, it can take only four or five days. Product design will be in the bag after four to five days.

Design Thinking in many ways replaces classic market research and target group analysis. What a customer really wants often remains a mystery with these methods, whereas Design Thinking can often unearth very authentic consumer demands.

The Six Fundamental Capabilities that Can Get your Digitization Started

Let us now embark upon this seemingly impenetrable multi-track voyage by focusing on the critical building blocks every corporate journey towards digital involves. There are six "no-regret" capabilities virtually every business can set up in uncomplicated ways to instantly milk advantages from digitization. No matter what, investing in these six capabilities will be worthwhile.

Figure 4.5 – Six "No-Regret" Capabilities[5]

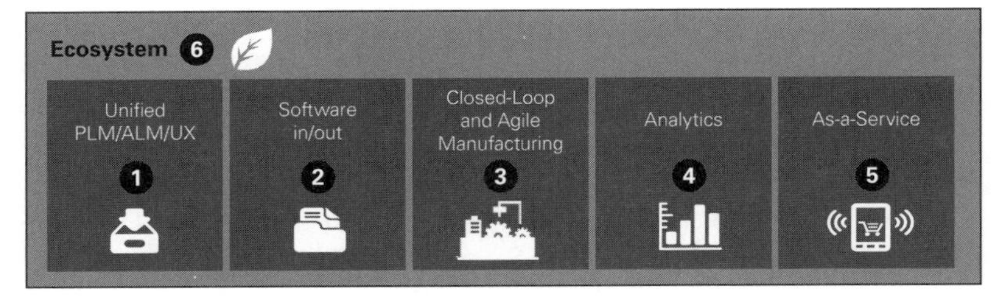

Together, the six capabilities constitute the foundations on which a fully-fledged IIoT economy will stand. However, at first, crucially, in line with the flexible, small-scale approach I have been advocating, they should all be individually implemented experimentally at project scale and a low-key entry level.

I advise doing this in a real business. This allows executives, staff and teams to get a feel for them and learn about their efficiency gains and value-creating power. This is better than you simply imposing a completely new world on staff wholesale. Small-scale implementation can spark further ideas for next steps, bottom-up. And all this can be done without committing enormous budgets. However I still believe the more disruptive the digitization move turns, the more it seem advisable to move this new business out of the mainstream and run it as a standalone operation.

One size does not fit all. Each business, enterprise culture and legacy is different. Operating models vary hugely between sectors such as automotive, pharmaceutical, utilities and industrial engineering. Each of our suggested six themes therefore have different starting points, speeds and budgets in an initial campaign for digitization across enterprise functions. We will discuss the variables for different industries in later chapters.

Try the capabilities out individually and push them forward if they work for you. The ones you're not ready for you can put on the backburner. Do be sure to test-drive every one of them, however; eventually, no enterprise will be able to do without any of them, as the Outcome Economy is unavoidable. But "eventually" is very different from "next week." There is time for your business to find its way, and it's vital that you take that time.

Start with each of the building blocks individually. Each one will provide benefits. Soon you will find combining two or more gives you exponential benefit. To reiterate: start small, but scale fast with what you find bolsters efficiency.

I will now briefly walk you through our six "no-regret" capabilities, which we will be able to study in action in the following chapters in much greater detail.

1. Synchronize your lifecycle clocks. Digital technologies advance fast, markets follow suit and in this fiercely competitive environment, a superior Product Lifecycle Management (PLM) approach is vital. Integrating the way you manage your hardware and software application lifecycles is key to this and is one of the most important "no-regret" capabilities we recommend. As you venture into digitization, your business's hardware, products, shop floor machines and other productive assets will age more slowly than the software that steers them. The way out of this dilemma is more integration and synchronization of hardware and software development cycles early on, something that has not yet happened in many industrial businesses with a legacy of unconnected products. Only this will spare you surprises in the shape of badly coordinated hardware and software features at a later stage in your development path. Surging demand for digitally connected cars, for instance, offers fresh horizons for manufacturers, yet also greatly increases complexity. Keep in mind that in today's cars, core components are revamped every seven to ten years while design parts retain topicality for a maximum of three to five years. Vehicle software on the other hand is up-to-date for only around two years, with new releases every six months. Getting all this different aging in step is best done by adopting a fully integrated PLM – a digital PLM, or DPLM – serving as a hub for product development. It allows car manufacturers to disseminate varied data among all critical functions such as engineering, product development, supply chain management, manufacturing, services and marketing – all in order to get the various clocks in step.

2. Embed software intelligence and connectivity within the traditional "dumb metal sheet product" in order to enable interaction with its environment such as people or machines, including other connected products. We already see the beginning of this formative trend. The bare hardware item, be it product or shop floor machine, will eventually fade away as a value creator and become a mere container. It will be the software intelligence attached that will define quality in a product or machine and high-margin prices on its market. A few companies are already on board with this. Domestic appliance maker Bosch Siemens Hausgeräte aims at making all their products smart and connected in a few years time.[6] Creating connected products and arranging production processes around connected machines means that software will eventually function like an all-enveloping muscle tissue, bringing arrangements of various hardware items to life. The rewards can be huge from this capability. German industrial engineering giant Siemens, for instance, operates an small electronics plant in southern Germany that was

25 percent automated in 1990 and has now reached 75 percent digital automation. Its defect rate has dropped to below 11.5 items per million produced and plant output has increased 8.5 times with little change to employment.[7]

3. Use analytics to get insight and decision support from data gathered by connected products and other data sources. This is probably the 21st century's ultimate "no-regret" capability. Unhindered data flow, data gathering and data analytics will soon be the profitable mainstay of highly digitized businesses. Imagine products that can broadcast location, performance and current condition to their makers. Real-time information can be about everything from how customers behave and what they discuss and prefer, to the performance and wear-and-tear levels of machines and products and the kind of disruption that can occur in manufacturing. The ability to acquire all this data will create huge business value in the future. Legacy investments in separated information and operational technology set-ups currently prevent companies from fully realizing the potential. However, once connected products or physical assets are developed and linked to networks and start to transmit data, new analytics methods can help reshape business models or create entirely new businesses. Many businesses have large amounts of historic data that can be fed through analytics engines to generate great insights. A manufacturer that does not tap into data analytics, even at project levels, will be at a major disadvantage. US heavy equipment manufacturer Caterpillar has recognized this, building a telematics solution that allows its customers to monitor its fleet in real-time, identify maintenance needs swiftly, and replace parts fast. It collects a vast amount of real-time data from machines, which proves invaluable in optimizing resources such as capacity, fuel and operators.[8]

4. Render your manufacturing facilities agile. Use industrial automation wherever possible to increase your shop floor's speed and flexibility. Automation is already transforming manufacturing in the automotive and industrial equipment industries, with sensors and control mechanisms now embedded in most machinery. What's more, increasingly, such devices are mostly connected to management, execution, logistics and ERP systems via the industrial cloud, so that analytics can be applied. Manufacturers have thus gained unprecedented oversight of and insight into the factory production process, enabling various efficiency measures. They can, for instance, identify and predict performance bottlenecks and breakdown points in machinery, improve compliance, boost availability, minimize waste, accelerate plant turnarounds, pilot new processes more effectively, and make smarter decisions about how to manage a more connected and collaborative workforce. Similarly, 3D Printing can boost repair and maintenance speed and help reduce the need for a spare parts inventory. Furthermore, integration of manufacturing to upstream PLM/ALM accelerates the whole design, development and manufacturing chain, so that the feedback from insights from analytics can be incorporated into future offerings.

5. Push for transition to as-a-service business models. "Everything as a service" is becoming the paradigm of the future Outcome Economy whereby combinations of products and services will no longer need to be acquired as property. Instead, they will simply be used flexibly – as-a-service – when required. This is because, as industrial devices become more intelligent and connected, they will produce large amounts of data, which can form the basis of a whole range of new data- and service-based business models. This derives from "no-regret" capability number two. Connected products can lead to data-based services as long as supporting digital infrastructure is also developed that can be reconfigured in different combinations to spawn new value chains and networks. For example, connectivity and smart devices enabled French tire manufacturer Michelin to move some of its business from selling tires to ensuring the mobility and safety of tires as a service. With intelligent sensors embedded in the tires, performance and lifecycle is monitored and coordinated to ensure replacement when needed.

Michelin thus created a new business line generating incremental revenues without cannibalizing its core tire sales business. This puts it in a position to adapt to the new, more service-based economy as it develops.[9]

6. Create ecosystems and run them. No single company will be in a position to own the whole digital value chain in an advanced stage of the Outcome Economy. In the fully evolved IIoT world, globally dispersed, "borderless" enterprises will orchestrate and run their multi-dimensional ecosystems of suppliers, customers, technology partners, start-ups, academia, competitors, contractors, dealers and distributors. All these will be parts of a symbiotic, porous business entity sitting at the heart of a business ecosystem. Seeing the big picture, enabling the ecosystem, bringing it all together, will be a collaborative endeavour by company executives. Combining their product and customer insight with the process and technology expertise of external industry partners will then be more the norm than the exception. Competition between companies will be replaced by competition between dynamic digital ecosystems and their central players. Fortunately, companies will no longer need to have all or even most of their digital capabilities in-house. But dynamically assembling such capabilities will become a critical competitive advantage. Being able to analyze, develop options and implement participation models within ecosystems are as new and critical capabilities typically required by companies. Such mindsets are light years away from tradition supplier management disciplines that may have worked well in the past, but will not translate into the new era.

Engineering Specialist Biesse Group Moves from Product to Services

Catering for a global niche market, the traditional Italian-based engineering firm Biesse Group, that employs around 3,800 staff and has a turnover of €618m, is aiming to achieve more revenue from selling services around their flagship products: special machinery for cutting wood, stone and glass. A further goal is to bring down warranty cost by leveraging data insights gathered from its installed base to improve its engineering designs.

In a first step, the company decided in 2016 to connect the machines they delivered to clients, using a software platform.

After a first successful pilot, the Biesse Group has now increased the number of connected machine, aiming to reach around ca. 10,000 machines connected in 2019 out of the 50,000 globally installed. Each machine is fitted with around 40 sensors and is connected, and now reports 60,000 events or eight megabytes of data per day back to the company, where it is analyzed.

The company's primary aim is to develop and hone its preventive, and eventually predictive analytics capability and thus reduce machine downtime altogether or even avoid it.

For this purpose, a team of data scientists have helped to develop a system of around 50 rules, each triggering an alarm, for instance when a certain temperature level in a machine is surpassed. Based on this, the Biesse Group can now sell an analytics service product named Connected Service 4.0 to their clients.

This forms the basis for a fully developed data loop, helping the Biesse Group's engineers to improve their machine designs and eventually get into a quicker innovation cycle and much more data applications. For this purpose, the following future use cases have been identified: condition-based management, product improvement analysis, automatic software distribution, energy and consumption management, usage-based pricing models, third-party machine services, and parts forecasting. This non-exhaustive list demonstrates that the first building block of a data-strategy forms the foundation for a much broader portfolio of applications and services.

Figure 4.6 – The Move from Product to Services for an Industrial Manufacturer[10]

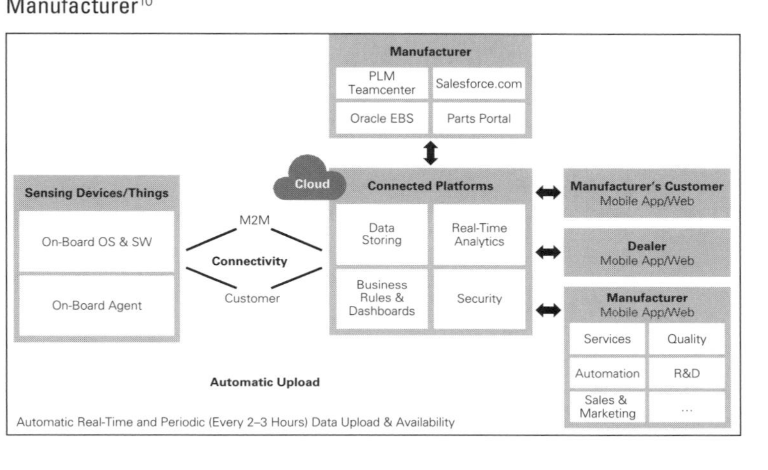

Your IIoT Business – How to Succeed

For many organizations, achieving end-to-end ownership through a data-driven business model will be challenging. The experiences of businesses in the electronic high-tech sector reveal five common pitfalls:

1. Applying "traditional" product innovation approaches in a situation that requires, instead, a dramatic re-think.

2. Developing IIoT initiatives that prioritize technology before exploring and validating the business case.

3. Choosing ecosystem partners without developing adequate participation models.

4. Investing too heavily in technology solutions and not enough in business capabilities.

5. Underestimating the criticality of analytics and data.

6. Underestimating the impact of a Connected Business transformation (explained below) on the operating model.

To avoid these dead ends, businesses should first develop a clear picture of the customer journey. Thus armed, they can align it with those aspects of their business that customers don't see, but that nevertheless can make or break the customer experience: internal operations and technology infrastructure.

The IIoT is critical to this digital transformation and it requires a shift in mindset – from connected product to connected service. To capture value, organizations will need to address emerging customer needs predictively and leverage the information convergence that enables the personalized, contextual, innovative services that drive recurring revenues. In other words, a "minimal lovable product" has to be created and hence a set of business capabilities is needed that can provide a meaningful customer experience able to keep evolving.

An IIoT-driven Connected Business transformation strategy focuses on a full-cycle transformation, from ideation to operations. In order to succeed here, organizations need to acquire both origination capabilities with a strong emphasis on Open Innovation partnerships, and delivery capabilities that leverage design thinking and a fast-prototyping approach – as well as technological capabilities.

To Take Services to Market, Think Big, Start Small, Scale Fast

The realistic roadmap for an initial Connected Business transformation strategy comprises three phases, which should be customized to the needs of each individual organization:

Phase 1: Launch a First Pilot and Create the Foundations (4-6 months)

1. Ideation / Incubation / Fast prototyping process – and ability to create value / work together – but with a limited scope

2. In parallel, shape the IIoT vision and partnership approach. Decide on

   - scope of customer experience, digital manufacturing, new services and business models

   - business capabilities to be implemented

   - enablers to be developed, such as analytics or an IIoT platform.

   - a global business case and business roadmap for digital service capabilities

   - your preferred partnership model

Phase 2: Industrialize – Grow (12-16 months)

3. Set up the key required partnership capabilities (e.g. IIoT digital factory)

4. Making sure to track outcomes and delivered value, start to implement and execute business and technology capabilities such as

   - ideation

   - incubation and fast prototyping

   - industrialization

   - analytics

Phase 3: Scale (12-24 months)

5. Jointly managed across the full digital services initiatives portfolio.

The promise of such an IIoT-driven Connected Business transformation strategy is clear: a two- to three-fold reduction in time to market and an exponential increase in incremental revenues. By following this three-phase roadmap, organizations can strengthen their chances of achieving such outcomes.

Takeaways

1. Digitally transforming your company is a challenging task that may look like a scary upheaval of all functions.

2. No perfect or predefined roadmap exists, but that doesn't mean to do nothing. Figuring out the perfect and detailed roadmap for your company is near to impossible and of little value. Set the high-level directions for your company and dive in.

3. Start-up-style rapid experimentation is the way to go. The rule of "deploy if successful, move on to the next idea if not" is standard in these firms. There should ideally be multiple rapid-experimentation sites across your enterprise to get the digital ball rolling.

4. There are six core "no-regret" capabilities to be targeted for the first steps towards a full-blown IIoT-powered enterprise: synchronizing the lifecycle clocks, embedding software intelligence and connectivity, using data analytics, rendering manufacturing facilities agile, understanding business as a service, creating and running smart ecosystems.

5. Try out each of these six "no-regret" capabilities and then combine. The benefits will only increase as you do so. This will contribute to quick wins and long-term success.

05

Chapter 5

Zoom in: How to Make Data Analytics Work Your Way

Big data creates the challenge of finding a way to deal with massive and quickly accumulated digital information loads. This is nowhere more palpable than in modern industrial manufacturing. Data, and the operational as well as commercial insights extracted from them, are going to be the lifeblood of the industrial sector in the 21st century. The most prominent task for businesses and their managers at all levels over the coming years will be to separate the digital data wheat from the chaff. It will be all about creating the right type of data, harvesting "smart data" by feeding raw data through adequate analytics tools and using them to arrive at decisions for better operational efficiency and market positioning. Sharing data insights within platforms will be a necessity no business can live without.

In the world of the Industrial Internet of Things (IIoT), everything and everybody will be connected – from consumers in sensor-rich environments to enterprises harnessing new technologies like robotics and machine learning.

This will produce enormous data tides waiting to be filtered and analyzed to gain actionable insights. Without good data analytics, the tide will simply engulf us, with no benefits to the business.

The global quantity of data is doubling every two years. By 2020, according to estimates, there will be more than 44 zetabytes of data in the world, of which 35 percent will be considered useful for analysis. By 2025 the amount will have grown to 180 zetabytes.[1]

The biggest proportion of this almost unimaginable load will be produced and analytically processed within smartened-up industrial enterprises and their ecosystems. For manufacturers, therefore, there is no alternative to the timely gathering and analyzing of data, as it will be the lifeblood of a grown-up Outcome Economy based on services around physical hardware.

Raw Data Has no Value and Needs Enrichment

At elementary levels, we all often use smartened-up data. Your car dashboard shows raw data such as vehicle speed, fuel level and engine revolutions per second. Rather than letting you draw your own conclusions, however, there is another gauge showing you how much fuel is burned at your current speed. This is basic real-time analytics: the three shreds of raw data are aggregated into smart and actionable information.

In the future this relatively elementary analytics will expand to include real-time weather conditions, landscape topology, traffic

Figure 5.1 – Technology Infusing the Enterprise and Implications[2]

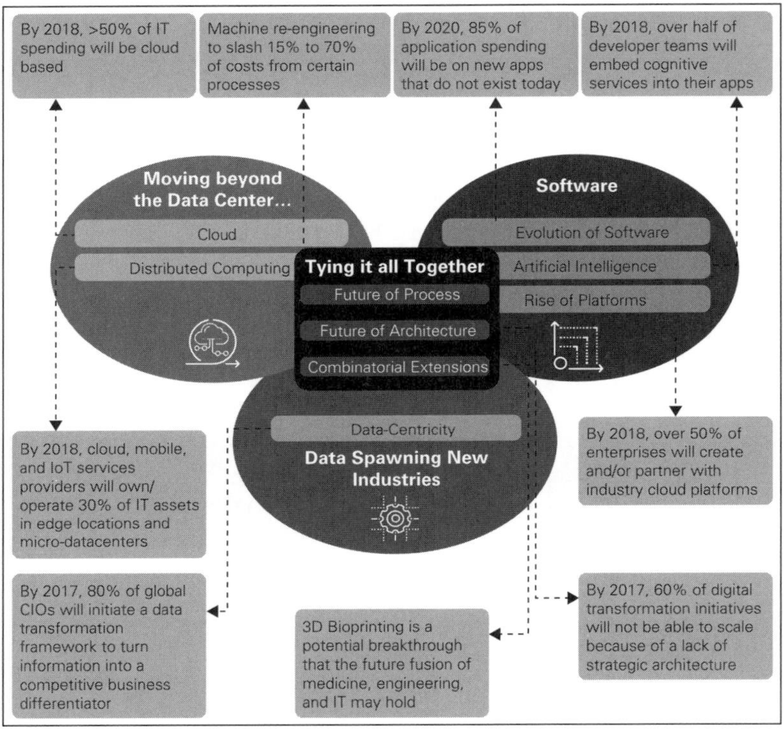

forecasts and remaining journey distance, all aggregated to make data-based recommendations.

The same applies for industrial businesses. Smartly filtered data is any kind of not yet analyzed data fed through analytical interpretation so decisions can be made. In most cases it is created by the algorithmic mincing of various unrelated readings to create a higher meaningful degree of information.

Compacting, cleaning, rehashing, filtering and grouping digital data delivers the insights and warnings needed to steer a complex manufacturing process effectively. The more ambitious analytics gets, the more software sophistication and computing power will need to be involved in data preparation, enrichment and, eventually, insights.

Figure 5.2 – The Data Value Chain[3]

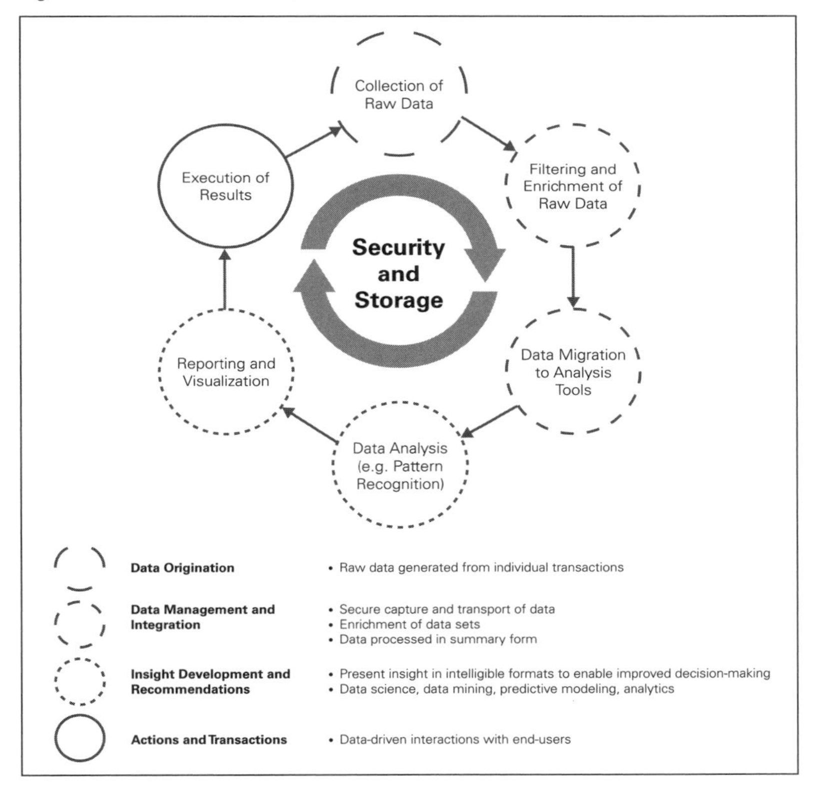

Which Data Strategy to Pursue – More Return from Inside or Outside?

We are also seeing more and more companies successfully monetizing data. It is happening in two principal ways.

On the one hand, enterprises are beginning to be able to read accurate conclusions from data insights produced across their own functions and processes. This allows them to improve their operational models and extract more value from them.

On the other hand, businesses are increasingly able to gather data insights from products used in the field, translate this into services and make these a mainstay of their value creation.

Danish wind turbine maker Vestas, for example, analyzes weather data to help situate and operate turbines for optimal energy output. In other words, they no longer just sell the product, but also offer a service for maximizing that product's use – on the back of predictive and asset performance analytics.[4]

For you as an industrial company with, let us assume, not much data strategy in place, the question is therefore whether to choose one of these strategies or mix them.

The following matrix table (Figure 5.3) shows a pool of analytics based across all business functions. Though not exhaustive, it gives a sense of the multitude of fields in which data analytics can add value. For more detailed practical examples, see Chapter 4's case studies on the data analytics strategies of Schneider Electric and Biesse.

The truth is, we are moving fast into a world where digital data will be the real corporate currency. Data analytics enables all industrial sectors to find impressive value pools. Just look at car manufacturers where data analytics could unlock up to 46 percent of the trapped value from an overall digitization strategy, as our calculation shows (see Chapter 3).

Figure 5.3 – Industrial Analytics Use Cases[5]

Customer Insight Driven	Supply Insight Driven			Aftersales			Asset Management
Innovation & Product Engineering	Manufacturing	Materials/ Supply Intl	Logistics	Warranty & Quality	Spare Parts	Customer Services	
Control Tower (Demand Sensing, Inventory Optimization, E/MOQ)							
Connected Business Analytics (Analytic Specific Solution Covering Process End-to-End)							
Product Portfolio Optimization	Digital Manufacturing Cockpit	Inventory Optimization (Part of CT)	Flow Path Optimization	Warranty Analytics	Spare Parts Forecasting	Predictive Maintenance Solution for Fleet Management	Root Cause Analytics
R&D Control Tower	Root Cause Analysis for PRD Quality	E/MOQ (Part of CT)	Service Level Optimization	Warranty Fraud Detection	Spare Parts Inventory Optimization	Customer Service Analytics	Predictive Maintenance Optimization
Development Time/Cost Analytics	Predictive Asset Maintenance	Replenishment Optimization		Warranty Early Warning	Spare Parts Pricing Optimization	Dealer Performance Analytics	Asset Reliability
Size & Pack Optimization		Contract Management		Early Anomaly Detection for Connected Products			Field Force Optimization
PRD Complexity/ Parts Rationalization		Procurement Analytics					
Embedded Software Analytics							

The Five Sources of Value that Can be Tapped with a Data Strategy

To refine the choice a little, we can isolate five major value-driving advantages from analyzing data for the industrial sector.

1. Optimized customer experience. Condensing data transmitted from connected products to feed into actionable insights can create instant value for companies, including manufacturers, their customers and their customers' customers. For instance, a car able to receive automatic software updates overnight from its manufacturer based on the data it transmits refreshes, changes and hence dramatically improves driver experience. To know "what is now" and "what will be next" is the big opportunity data analytics offers. According to similar principles, customer experiences are being instantly improved by industrial lifecycle services such as those offered by the global industrial equipment manufacturer group Schneider Electric and other players for industrial plants, wind farms and building compounds. Data-extracted customer profiling allowing for services adapted to individuals is steadily growing in the industrial sector.

2. Optimized product performance. A connected product, brought to life by software, can offer much more value than non-smart hardware. Smart energy meters in combination with data analytics allow utilities to achieve much more effective grid and energy management. Warranty management can be streamlined via artificial intelligence applications and crunches of data coming from connected products and their components on performance. Connected components in industrial machines allow for precise predictions about when each part will need to be inspected, maintained or replaced. Heavy lorry components supplier ZF Friedrichshafen offers a compelling example. It developed a fuel-economic transmission system that knows in advance when to shift gears, by analyzing the topography on the basis of a GPS data feed.[6]

3. Optimized workforce efficiency. Data analytics can obviously help a lot with managing people in industrial sectors. Oilfield workers will be safer as they are monitored through wearable tags. Water utilities can use predictive analytics to forecast pipe ruptures, keeping engineers safe. Applying analytics to worker tag data can not only heighten safety but optimize overall downtime by better optimizing complex field interventions. US manufacturing service firm Jabil, for instance, reduced monthly close time by 50 percent and manual handling through its finance teams by as much as 70 percent after it installed a large-scale analytics solution.[7]

4. Optimize operational efficiency. Applying advanced analytics to raw industrial data can of course help a great deal with optimizing overall operational efficiency. Consumption of water, energy and raw materials can be fine-tuned to a minimum by applying data analytics, while logistics fleets inside and outside manufacturing plants can be brought to maximum productivity and machinery can be maintained according to efficient schedules. However there is much more to this. Shop floor assets can be given an optimal maintenance cycle, product portfolios optimized and warranty costs reduced through data analytics

5. Optimize the portfolio of new products and services. Data analytics forms the basis for entirely new customer propositions. In the industrial sector, data insights can be used to create numerous new services around hardware products, new services around managed operations and new approaches to marketing and commercial trade with data itself. There are companys using their software to collect data as the basis of new maintenance services.

IoT Lead Generation – Anticipate your Customers' Demand

Many industrial and electrical equipment manufacturers have huge data loads on their installed base that they do not use. This means they are sitting on an untapped goldmine.

Initiatives are being launched by several of these manufacturers. Leveraging their existing investments in IT/OT infrastructure, they are combining customer and installed base knowledge to generate new revenue streams, increase the efficiency of their field force, and enhance their overall customer experience.

By exploiting existing data, often currently stored in their enterprise IT systems, they are generating valuable insights in terms of (1) potential cross – and up-selling opportunities, (2) work order generation for field intervention, (3) increase of service contract yield (condition base contracts, contract renewal) or (4) warranty renewals.

Figure 5.4 – Lead Generation Analytics from a Real-Life Example[8]

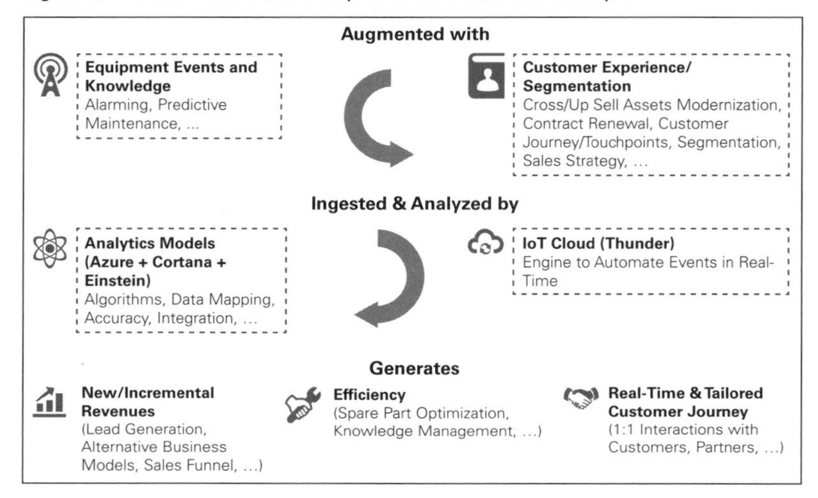

This first step will already bring immense value while requiring minimal additional investment (except for a first pilot to convince the organization of the benefits, and for development of the first algorithms). But imagine the business value generated when such an intelligent infrastructure is connected directly to the installed base, activating data on a real-time basis.

Data can then be collected from anywhere, meaning from the manufacturers operational systems, directly from the connected equipment on the shop floor or in the field, or any other source for that matter. The ingested data is transformed and normalized to build 360° views of each customer and the equipment they have installed. It is then processed through predefined business rules, driving proposed commercial actions that can be executed automatically (business lead, work order, etc.) or routed to the field force or customer service for specific intervention.

But how do you set such a platform? How do you leverage your existing IT investments? Customer relationship management tools, such as Salesforce or Microsoft CRM, can be connected to the manufacturer's products in the field. Via specific analytics, this creates insights into customer behavior and preferences around specific services or products from the manufacturer.

Figure 5.5 – Closing the Loop in the Ecosystem[9]

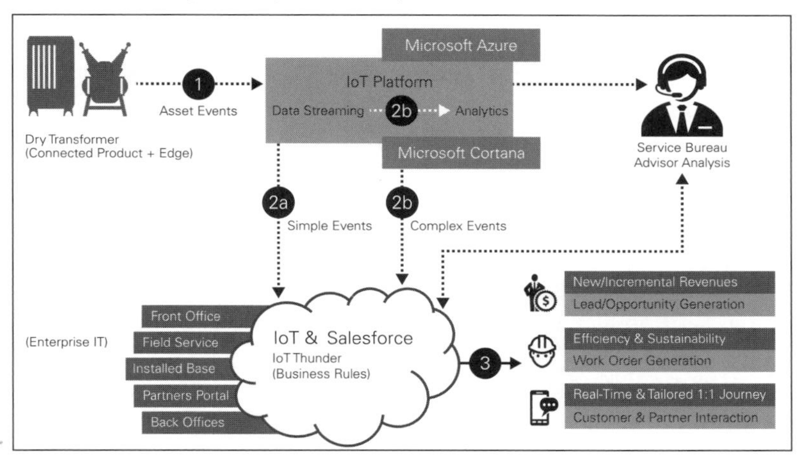

The solution is extremely flexible and scalable and universally adaptable to various industrial-sector businesses as well as powered by a simple analytics platform.

The business case is strong. Working with several manufacturers in this field, revenue uplift is expected in the range of 10-15 per cent via increasing number and quality of leads, improvement of conversion ratios, and increased customer retention and stickiness. And this does not account for the reduction in sales cost and acceleration of the sales cycle.

From Mere Monitoring to a Real Predictive Maintenance Practice

As a general rule of thumb, the greatest value created by data analytics in industrial manufacturing is found around physical assets.

Detecting location is probably the most common use case so far. To know where a certain physical asset, component, mobile machine, tool or person is in a supply chain, on a shop floor, or out in the field is very value-rich because all that information can be directly translated into efficiency gains.

The second most common use case is probably data analytics finding real-time answers to questions such as whether machines are running properly and assembly lines and robots are functioning within their defined tolerances.

Over time this will develop from mere monitoring to a more predictive maintenance practice and eventually to pre-emptive functions where the failure of a certain mechanical component can be forecast from collected sensor data or avoided altogether by improving the component's quality.

A Global Heavy Equipment Manufacturer Moves into the Realms of Connected Services

A leading global manufacturer for construction, mining as well as power generation equipment, was an early adopter of IoT, yet, over the years their capabilities needed a major and rapid overhaul – from cost structure and business model, to architecture and technical capabilities.

Additionally, the key industries that the company serves – mining, construction, oil and gas, and others – are all challenged, and focusing heavily on asset effectiveness. Therefore, they needed to pivot heavily towards outcomes enabled by technology, not just machines, which are no longer the differentiator.

First they developed and aligned on a compelling IoT vision – from business models, to solution architecture, development and operation of new, digitally enabled services.

Leveraging off-the-shelf, future-flexible, cloud-based, connected platforms, their journey was significantly accelerated. In a matter of weeks, the prototype applications were talking to physical devices in the field, and today there are hundreds of thousands of direct connections and millions of sensors on their customers' machines and equipment, globally, and billions of transactions annually.

Enabled by high-speed, two-way communications, the company now offers a new generation of advanced services such as over-the-air software updates, remote monitoring, troubleshooting and machine configuration, and enabling of autonomous technology, to name a few.

These technologies form the foundation for the next generation of services – combining real-time data from sensors, dealers, and the broader enterprise – to deliver predictive failure detection and proactive lead management, allowing the company to create significant value for their customers.

Data Analytics Strategy – the New Industrial Must-Have

There are, all in all, five fast-moving technologies driving the current data and data analytics boom in today's industrial factories. All propel the instant creation, rapid relay and swift analytical processing of digital data in the industrial sector.

First, there is the remote processing power of cloud computing, offering businesses unprecedented scalability, flexibility and responsiveness in running their enterprise processes based on digital data.

Second, there is the emergence of advanced software analytics at huge capacity and new data velocity allowing for wide-ranging real-time insights by filtering massive volumes of operational data.

Third, there are more and more self-regulating sensor-and-actor networks for machine control emerging, with ever-greater sophistication and ever larger data throughputs.

Fourth, the trend towards "connected everything" creates new modes of automated and personal interaction – for instance between customers or members of the workforce.

Fifth, social media data drives real-time marketing and new ways of collaborating within and well beyond the organization.

Let us briefly focus on real business life, where we will see that foregoing a data analytics strategy is no longer an option for industrial enterprises.

Industrially made products are slowly but surely enveloped with huge amounts of data-collecting sensor technology. Modern aircraft or train locomotives, for example, count sensors in their thousands in order to give their makers and users a broad-based data picture showing actions to be taken or design or service improvements to be made.

At this point there are even lots of great examples of companies such as Uber and Airbnb that extract their value exclusively from digital data rather than leveraging physical assets. They are active in sectors that previously seemed impossible to disrupt because of their assumed physical nature. Nobody thought that you could run the world's biggest hotel business while not owning a single hotel, or the world's largest taxi company without possessing a taxi.

There is every reason to believe that specialized smart analytics companies could be disruptors in the industrial space too, without owning physical products or assets.

Imagine, for instance, being the manufacturer of an industrial pump used in sectors such as utilities or mining. If an innovative start-up sticks sensors and matching analytics software to your pumps installed in the field, they will be able to collect data from them that could have been yours and offer services based on it to your clients.

This is a huge risk for all equipment manufacturers, their products hugely losing value as others commoditize their data. The objective for both manufacturers and start-ups in this space will be to capture or keep by any available means access to the end customer. Only this gives you sovereignty over your valuable data. That is why you have to start working out your data strategy now – so you can do it on your own terms.

Gains to Make Now in a Changing Landscape

In many cases industrial enterprises need not start from scratch when taking the first steps towards a comprehensive data strategy. We often find in the industrial equipment sector that products are already heavily instrumented with sensor technology. Equipment users can collect and use data in principle but don't yet do it. Or they might have gathered and stored data without running analytics on it.

Take modern mining operations. Manufacturers fit most of the equipment with data technology by default. They have mobile or WiFi connectivity across the mine, monitoring all the trucks, crushers and conveyor belts, as well as the ground and geology.

However, these data streams often run in contained silos without the connection and aggregation necessary for applying data analytics. In such companies you typically find around 50 control room screens fed by individual equipment providers. These are inadequate for the pit supervisor to tell whether the mine has hit its shift production target or not – a typical example of big data with minimal insight.

That in mind, a first step towards improvement would be trawling existing data stock for insights. Next, the business could experiment with processing fresher data to prepare the stage for what is cutting edge today: getting insights from real-time operational data.

Data can be consolidated by analytics into key performance indicators and actionable information. This, after being refined in real-time, can be put on an at-a-glance tablet screen that can be carried around by the supervising personnel.

In this way, sense would be made of what is otherwise a blur of disparate data from multiple sources.

Across manufacturing sectors, there is a key preparatory step to be made before marketable digital services and internal operational processes can be based on smart data: siloed and circulatory data loops and systems need to be broken up and merged or interconnected. Fortunately, recent technological advances hugely facilitate this.

Digital technology has matured enough to translate big data effectively into actionable knowledge – for instance, by tying together data steering of decentralized control systems at different plant sites. What's more, embedded sensors and control mechanisms already power much shop-floor machinery these days.

Thanks to the convergence of operational technology (OT) and information technology (IT) – the link up between data networks commanding machines and robots with the IT systems backing up the whole enterprise – machine and device fleets can often be found connected with formerly unrelated data systems such as production management, manufacturing execution, logistics and enterprise planning.

Manufacturing Execution Systems (MES), track and document how raw materials are transformed into goods. In many industrial sectors these systems, formerly scattered across plant sites, are now orchestrated under one control unit with Enterprise Asset Management systems (EAM) monitoring machine life cycles and the business's other physical components.

This gives many manufacturers real-time visibility into their production process. And, though the capacity is still limited, analytics allows them to identify and predict performance bottlenecks and make smarter decisions about how to improve factory operations, and manage workforce and supply chain risks.

Soon we will see further business functions being built into such embryonic enterprise backbones giving businesses the precise availability of raw materials outside the company or an exact account of customer specifications for products in use in the field. At this stage, industrial operations will become even more flexible, cost-efficient and capable of delivering highly tailored outcomes.

Once again, the message is: though the landscape is still developing, and developing fast, there are immediate gains to be made from implementing what is available. As always, start small and scale up fast with what works for you.

How Utility Businesses Harness Big Data Analytics

Consider the example of a large water supplier catering for a big capital city of around nine million people. This is a good case in point as the company has collected data based on a mix of self-made and third-party IT solutions at a large scale.

Crucially, insights were locally siloed at its various sites and plants, rendering its data analytics very ineffective and largely unconnected to its operational technology backbone. The company had spent $200m on a legacy IT solution that was not entirely connected and left them with fragmented decision-making and no central hub for decision support.

As a result, nobody had full visibility across all plants when it came to important operational data on water pressure, vibration, flow, chemical consumption, energy consumption, or timings around when a plant started and stopped treating water.

The company needed an umbrella analytics platform stretching across all 14 segments of its value chain, from tapping reservoirs to usage in households to managing waste water to disposal of treated water into the sea.

The investment, carried out at minimum level, delivered a return in under six months. The water supplier can now plan ahead and allocate resource much more effectively because weather data such as temperature and rainfall is included in the analytics. There is also more lead-time to react to data developments displayed on platform dashboards in real-time.

Within the company, a few hundred managers and over 1,000 workers now find it much easier to make decisions, resulting in the creation of around $63m of value per year. On top of that, the business reduced its operating expenses (OPEX) by up to eight percent while its expenditure on capital came down by up to 12 percent.

Keep Pilots Incremental and Focused

Many companies still believe that tying legacy data technology into smart actionable insights is troublesome and daunting. In fact, technological advances in data analytics, as in the case just described, render this view obsolete.

Today there is hardly any remaining need to standardize or normalize data before it can be fed through insight-creating algorithms. Statistical applications and database systems can receive, save and digest data in diverse mixes of structured or unstructured formats as well as various data types such as numerical, textual or visual. Even hugely diverse data from different generations of data collecting technology have stopped being a big problem.

So where does enterprise reality stand with data analytics and what is the right approach to building that capacity?

Most industrial enterprises are currently moving into a world where they are starting to see but are not yet entirely confident in articulating the principal advantages of a data strategy and data analytics in particular.

One therefore sees a lot of companies piloting analytics projects and trying to learn from them as they go. Indeed "start small and scale fast" is the only way to build data analytics capability in a phase where the relevant technological development is still progressing quickly.

Eventually, data analytics will follow the trajectory of other technologies. Twenty years ago companies all built their Customer Relationship Management (CRM) capability from scratch at huge cost and mostly on propriety IT foundations. Today, companies buy CRM as a fully developed cloud service, tailored and scaled as required, from third-party vendors.

This will eventually happen with data analytics, but for now the jury is still out on which industrial platforms will succeed as the dominant analytics provider. As in any other IT market, we will see consolidation among data analytics service providers for corporates. In a couple of years, CIOs and CTOs will be able to choose from a handful of well-established vendors and companies will be able to learn from each other's work.

All this means that in the current environment, it is sensible to stick to incremental steps in the shape of pilot projects focused on specific use cases (as shown in Figure 5.3) that will be scaled once they prove themselves. So start with small and focused analytics pilots but in as many areas of your company as possible.

How Car Manufacturers Scale Analytics

A European car manufacturer has grown massively over recent years and aims eventually to build a company-wide data analytics platform.

They started out with a confined analytics project around their quality and warranty system and eventually achieved a value-creation target of $100m annual savings, bringing down warranty management and repair costs by 20 percent.

The specific initial problem: Three percent plus of company turnover went on warranty repair – cars under three years old were covered – where leaders in the sector were spending two percent or less.

The carmaker aimed to improve vehicle quality and customer satisfaction while also reducing warranty cost by screening claims for plausibility. The task was to transform their warranty and quality management processes by leveraging a data analytics platform that provided sufficient transparency.

Masses of data were available to the manufacturer: millions of warranty claims, each made up of forms describing faults, diagnostic codes and spare parts affected. Dealer and connected vehicle diagnostic data was also available for some markets and vehicles.

Yet, the manufacturer was not analyzing this massive data load in an organized way, pinpointing individual technical problems and prioritizing issues, seeing, for instance, whether two or three or 100,000 vehicles were affected by a specific issue or establishing whether root causes were engineering or manufacturing problems.

With the new analytics platform, they can create their own high-resolution insights, prioritize their quality resolution projects and discuss them with their suppliers and engineering department. The company now pays only for genuine warranty cases and has brought down fault detection times.

The key point in looking at this as part of a longer-term strategy is that the analytics platform created for quality and warranty management can eventually be extended to give spare part makers better clues to improve quality – on a platform that would then span the whole value chain.

Flexible Data Analytics as a Service and Edge Computing

Starting with a confined data analytics project, to be scaled later, makes the case for cloud-based data solutions strong, as the risk of betting on the right technology is left completely with the cloud provider. To subscribe to data analytics as a service makes things even less complicated for the industrial sector.

As with data analytics service providers, it is still an open question which of the hundreds of cloud services will be the market leaders. But cloud services are distinct because initial investment in them is low as only limited in-house capability is built. Pilot and proof of concept costs are minimized and the freedom to exit a technology if it does not work for you is an additional plus. This makes it possible for you to include existing cloud providers as part of your company's small-scale, low-risk pilot projects.

At the same time, there are issues with cloud-based analytics that make them unsuitable in some situations. A large multi-national industrial company's data masses cannot always easily be bundled and sent off to the data cloud for insight extraction because the quantity of machine data collected from various sites for remote analytics will often just be too huge to serve as a useful real-time decision-making tool.

For example, vibration or temperature data from hundreds of machines across various locations cannot be shoved back and forth as quickly as is needed to give exactly the low-latency actionable insights needed. Or companies may not be able to afford a 99.9 percent cloud analytics availability.

Fortunately, not all enterprise data needs to be relayed to a centrally located processing server, as happens with cloud computing and the merging of operational and informational data networks within enterprises. The solution is to deploy more and more analytics close to the data-generating equipment – a relatively new concept called "edge computing," in which data crunching no longer always takes place in the back office. Instead, a decentralized data analytics landscape is formed across the enterprise, avoiding overly heavy data loads being processed in too few analytical hubs.

Figure 5.6 – Edge Analytics[10]

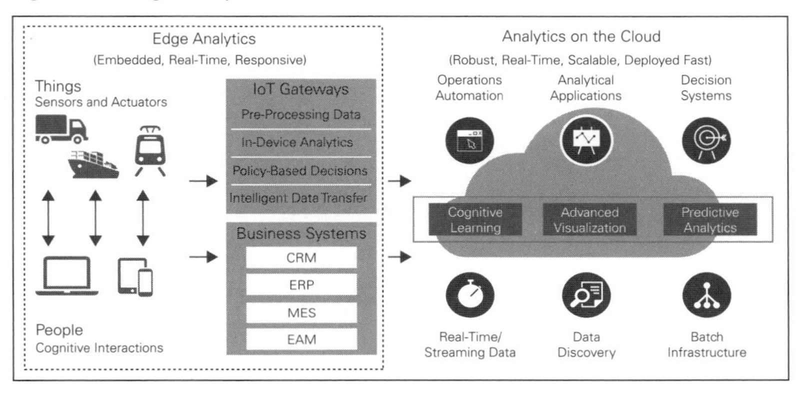

Due to its low-transport latency, edge computing can deliver better accuracy and timeliness. Analyzing data, software intelligence and automated decision-making is left to little processors able to run an independent machine regime that is still orchestrated with other such devices, forming a network of data islands.

Edge computing will also allow legacy systems to age gracefully, work autonomously and deliver information to decision-makers fast and efficiently. Manufacturers will be able to deploy data intelligence where it makes the most sense: in the field area network, at the edge device itself, or at broader enterprise levels.

Also, edge technology can fulfill many clients' desire to keep industrial data within the enterprise's borders, for instance where there is a worry about giving sensitive data to a third-party cloud service for analysis.

Data privacy and security regulation also come into play here, with differing rules in different parts of the world governing the extent to which data can traverse national borders or the confines of a business entity.

Of course, despite the clear trend towards these solutions, one should still aim for overall cross-functional data flow within a company to avoid silos. But the concept is definitely one of the most promising ways to arrive at smart industrial data insights.

Practically Connecting the Digital Factory

To achieve the IIoT's internal operational efficiency and data gains, a company's existing legacy physical assets and functions – its machines, assembly lines, and customer service units or truck fleets – need to be enveloped in a universal digital "tissue" that, through API gateways, allows for seamless flow and intelligent filtering and presentation of data throughout all relevant operations.

The effort to give the market such a universal and enveloping digital medium has been driven by the vendors of industrial engineering solutions and machinery.

On the one hand they provide edge computing, allowing for extensive analytics of all enterprise data. On the other hand they also provide an integrated platform for industrial companies to manage their main operational dimensions such as steering energy consumption, planning optimal machine downtime and optimizing material handling and supply chains.

These types of facilitating digital intermediaries will eventually provide the critical blood vessels and nerve pathways wrapping around the dumb bones of the IIoT. They will play the most important role when it comes to knocking down silos within businesses and enabling free data exchange, which will be necessary once we reach the Outcome Economy. Probably the biggest advantage is they will flexibly integrate your existing hardware and functionalities, entailing minimal investment in new technologies.

Again, it will be a while before the winners in this market emerge, but the big industrial machinery manufacturers stand a good chance.

If you think that it is still too early for you to start your digitization drive on one of the large industrial software platforms, you should go forward with individual more insular digitization projects.

A Leading Tire Manufacturer Harmonizes its Shop Floor Data Management Globally

A leading tire manufacturer is a global organization that runs more than 100,000 production machines in their factories all around the world. Over the years, the technical teams had created more than 800,000 codes for spare parts stocked to keep the machines up and running. This represents an inventory worth hundreds of millions of euros.

Finding the right part for a given repair plan while the machine was working – necessary to minimize production downtime – was a real pain point that made planning and scheduling maintenance a huge challenge.

Two large projects were launched to address these issues. In a first leg the more than 800,000 part codes were re-codified and classified in almost 800 classes with their technical attributes. This created a consistent and searchable catalogue of spare parts available to technicians and inventory specialists in 14 languages across the company's 70 sites.

A data governance process was set-up at regional and global levels to validate the creation of new codes. All the information was made available in an Enterprise Asset Management (EAM) solution that has been deployed through the second project over all the group's sites to 15,000 people.

The EAM solution supports planned and unplanned maintenance processes, parts inventory management and procurement, planning and scheduling as well as maintenance analytics.

Millions of work orders with unprecedented quality levels now go through the analytics platform to provide maintenance insights on the usage of parts and repetitive break-downs.

These two successful projects generate huge savings for the company through inventory reduction of more than 10 percent, increased machine availability (at least 25,000 fewer breakdowns per year), energy savings and maintenance cost reductions of more than €50m per annum.

Maintenance teams now have the right information, on the shop floor, at the right time, and have the levers to support continuous improvement.

Wherever you Start, Work Along a Roadmap for More

Although each project will form a test bed for further scaling, each should at any time fit into an overall strategic map. This is not to say that you must have a precise blueprint or timetable, something I have already said is neither possible nor desirable in this changing and fundamentally improvisatory landscape. It is about having a clear general outline of your objective – something that can all too easily get lost when running multiple pilots.

An objective will help you define the areas where your open-ended, exploratory pilots should run. Specifically, decide where analytics-derived value should be created internally via improved operational flows and externally through new customer service propositions.

Your strategy should always be two-pronged: leverage data analytics on the one hand to improve your operational efficiency in legacy strands of your business lines and on the other, always look at expanding revenues through up- or cross-selling new products and service propositions that are digitally based and designed.

Almost all industrial companies have a wealth of legacy data they are not leveraging. This is an important additional strand in a data strategy. Start progressively exploiting operational data hidden in your existing IT systems. Once the first pilots have delivered value you can integrate external data and, as your products get smarter and more connected, further enrich your data incrementally.

Clearly, much more than for purely consumer-facing sectors, these processes are complex for industrial companies. In general, working towards such clearly defined targets is best done by developing consistent overall client and connected product strategies while also, in tandem, experimenting with multiple pilot schemes.

The point is to run many different small-scale test schemes that ultimately aim to be part of a unified field. Your early map should consist of "islands" that can gradually integrate, forming land bridges to make them part of a continent. To do this, you need to be keeping an eye on both how each island works internally and how each will eventually work with the others. Keep it flexible enough at the outset that when one island scheme fails you can drop it and insert another into the overall big picture.

How Pharmaceutical Businesses Turn Data into Valuable Insights

A large multi-national pharmaceutical giant compellingly shows how end-to-end thinking can add value in data analytics.

The enterprise had no full view of its value chain. This was value-critical for a company with very slow roll-out, often spanning 2.5 years from first manufacturing step to patient delivery.

At the beginning of many of the company's processes is an active ingredient, perhaps in a quantity of around 50 liters. Each batch goes into different products in different areas of the world. It is tested repeatedly and diluted into various potencies. It goes into pills, creams and liquid applications, needs testing again, needs packaging, labelling, leafleting, warehousing – and is finally delivered to hospitals, pharmacies or patients.

This process is so complex that to find out at one central supervising point in real-time where a certain active ingredient was in the supply chain was almost impossible.

The company therefore deployed a hub-style data analytics platform by which each process step of each batch would be centrally visualized on a dashboard, securing an end-to-end view of the whole value chain. The solution used only the data already produced day-to-day but connected a multitude of dots to make the process chain transparent.

It is estimated that the impact on inventory value is several hundred million euros by this solution, which took only five months to install.

Clearly, the pharmaceuticals example is just one project, not many running in tandem, but in providing such a clear overview of so many complex operations, it gives an indication of the kind of project that could be key as you begin to build your big picture.

To exploit the data you collect, you will, of course, require the expertise of data scientists, personnel whose skills are now in high demand (as I discuss in Chapter 7). In that light, the best approach is to leverage your ecosystem of partners that have either these skills on board or "plug and play" solutions in their service catalogue.

Takeaways

1. Data and the operational and commercial insights extracted from it are going to be the lifeblood of the industrial sector in the 21st century.

2. All companies have a wealth of unleveraged legacy data. Enriching this data will drive significant value in five main areas: (a) customer experience, (b) product performance, (c) workforce efficiency, (d) operational efficiency, and (e) portfolio optimization of new products and services.

3. Start progressively exploiting operational data hidden in your existing IT systems. Once the first pilots have delivered value, integrate external data. As your products become smarter and more connected, make the direct link.

4. Launch small, safe analytics pilots focused on specific use cases. Do so in as many areas of your company as possible and scale your data platform as soon as success clicks in.

5. Set up a cross-enterprise analytics capability to support all these initiatives within your company. Leverage data analytics service providers to accelerate the process and run pilots targeting both top-line and bottom-line opportunities.

06

Chapter 6

Zoom in: How to Handle Digital Product Development

From idea generation and engineering to prototyping, testing and industrialization, the entire process chain around developing and designing industrially manufactured items is redefined by the emergence of the smart and connected product. Strong Digital Product Lifecycle Management (DPLM) must be the starting point for product development in the emerging era of data-driven Living Products that allow for responsive and hyper-personalized user experiences.

The term "connected product" refers to objects, devices and machines equipped with sensors, controlled by software and connected to the Internet. By default, connected products collect all types of valuable data about their specific usage modes, which they analyze and share with other devices. Thus, the evolutionary path of industrial products leads from the past – "dumb", static and detached pieces of physical hardware – towards the next phase of them being connected and software-intelligent, and then eventually to the stage of connected and communicative items tied into feedback loops with their users and their creators. If we include an adaptive user interface providing yet another level of experience, we arrive at a truly Living Product.

Figure 6.1 – Multiple Disruptions Across Industries Impacting R&D[1]

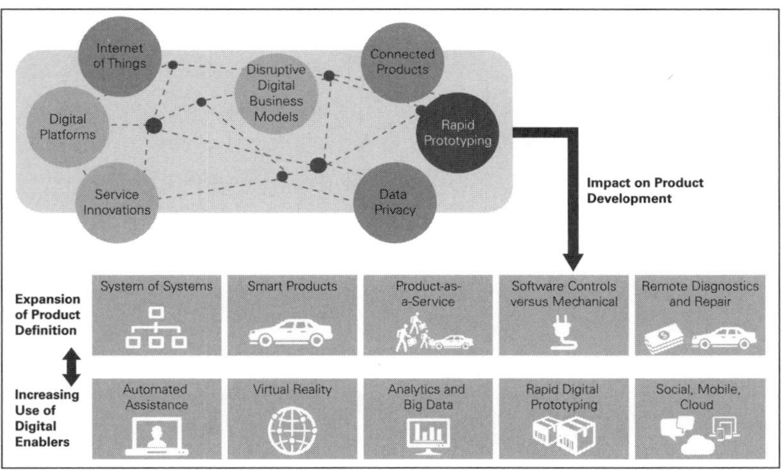

These radically new product characteristics will give rise to the Outcome Economy. Connectivity and software-centric services are what will eventually allow manufacturers to respond instantly to demand. To be ready for this, it is vital to adopt digitally empowered R&D processes and thus a new Product Lifecycle Management (PLM) approach.

In the future, industrial sector R&D must be conducted with the idea that data has become a commercially valuable product in itself. The value of connected products and the smart services they offer will be born from the platforms they provide for multi-partner software ecosystems enabling adaptive and personalizable user experiences.

From Connected Products to Digitized Product Development

I know of no sector where market research does not clearly indicate that companies will be financially better off providing connected, service-enabled products, rather than unconnected products in the future.

For instance, in a simulation of typical industrial equipment and automotive enterprises with revenues sales between $25bn and $55bn, it was found that proactive digital leaders in these two industries would boost EBITDA profits by between $1.2bn and $2.35bn. By contrast, the expected loss from doing nothing is around $850m for the carmaker and $490m for the industrial equipment business.[2]

As I write this book, technology giants like Amazon, Google, Apple, Samsung and others are involved in the early stages of a business and technology battle to establish themselves in the connected home.

Along with the evolution of the connected appliances themselves, the supremacy over the ecosystem and the experience in the connected home will have far-reaching consequences for these companies and the consumer alike.

An Appliance Manufacturer Conquers the Smart Home

The market of a leading appliance vendor is changing with the rapid emergence of the connected home. Producing products such as washing machines, coffee makers or vacuum cleaners, the business was able to bank for a long while on mechanical excellence. Now the appliances markets are noticeably shifting towards the concept of connected products within the context of the domestic Internet of Things (IoT).

Faced with these shifts, the main aim of the business is to create and sell useful services around its products, thus opening up new revenue streams. The challenge lies in the relatively complex set-up of smart home solutions where multiple vendors for different appliances are the norm. Many rivals are exploring the market in a similar way and no platform technology standard has yet emerged to serve as a bridging mechanism.

Still the company faces the challenge, convinced of the need and opportunities, and has chosen 2018-2020 as the key phase when all its new appliance ranges shall show advanced software content, connectivity and smart home compatibility. In parallel the vendor is driving forward its internal digital transformation, the improvement of the digital consumer experience of its products, and the digitization of its R&D function, sales channels and service lines.

Although it sounds technically simple to connect consumer items, there are numerous challenges when transforming established product features along with their related research and development processes. Engineers have to deal with a massive increase of software inside the product and face an explosion in the number of potential product variants as personalization and targeting of more refined customer groups becomes critical – a factor also increasing the need for much more flexible manufacturing processes.

There is now a need to think in categories of a software-reconfigurable product. Even domestic appliances' hardware elements require a degree of technological adaptability. The reliable distribution of software updates has to be organized and a customer registration and relations management mechanism created. All functions, from development to sales and service teams have to adapt to the re-configurability and new maintenance cycles of products. Last but not least, engineers have to keep an eye on cost by designing the appliance products along modularity.

Restructuring internal processes for digital poses similar challenges. Hardware and software engineering need strict alignment where previously they were relatively siloed. There is also a strong need for new interfaces among product development and manufacturing teams.

Overall, this company is going to need to ramp up intake of software engineers by up to five times.

Actually, domestic appliances, tires, postal packages, homes and many other items in day-to-day use have only gained a limited level of data intelligence and responsiveness. For instance, the health data measured by a sports wristband could, ideally, be relayed back to its manufacturers so they can offer targeted monitoring and training services to the owner. Yet, due to still limited mobile connection speed and computing capacity, this and many similar consumer propositions still only have preliminary test-the-market status and are far from what they could be in terms of mass-diffusion, complexity, response time, positively surprising experience and actual practical help for the user.

In the near future you and your ecosystem partners' value-adding services will be bundled with hardware to enhance the user experience. The world of interconnected objects – the IoT – will offer a pleasant, user-friendly experience when data transmission and processing speed allow for omnipresent real-time communication between user and object and object and service provider.

The incoming 5G mobile phone standard, operational from around 2020, and new generations of cloud-based computing power are promised to bring the world of connected products to life.[3] Hardware items will serve largely as containers of intelligent code, their functional quality defined by this software, their value judged by the efficiency of new human-machine co-operation, and the general user experience.

An elevator system in a corporate skyscraper will seem absurdly inefficient unless it is controlled by software identifying usage levels at different times and running less elevator units during quiet periods. A car will seem wildly old-fashioned if it cannot autonomously finds its way around Saint-Germain-des-Prés and recognize a particular passenger when she gets in, adjusting seat position, lighting and work or entertainment facilities for personal preference.

In the same vein, narrowing the focus to the Industrial Internet of Things (IIoT) a software-intelligent and highly sensorized robot – a collaborative robot or cobot – installed on an industrial shop floor, will adapt autonomously within seconds to a new human co-worker, counterbalancing individual weaknesses and augmenting forces.

In this light, it becomes clear how important it is to get connected or Living Product interfaces right. In design terms, attractive aesthetics for, say, touchscreens, are by no means enough. Usability is key and complex. Functionality must be highly adaptive to very individualized user situations. Navigation must be intuitive, straightforward and economical. In an industrial environment, interfaces for things like manufacturing machines or robots, must truly augment a user's natural physical or mental capabilities and thus enhance efficiency and experience at work.

Figure 6.2 – New Product Design and Architecture to Support Speed, Agility, and Hyperpersonalization[4]

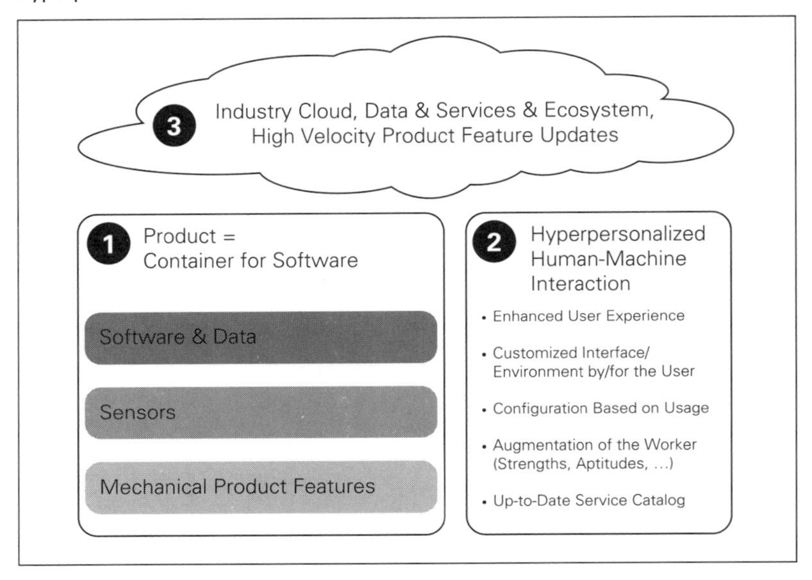

Industrial enterprises have already acted to prepare for the new era. IT market researcher Gartner has established that 40 percent of industrial products under development in 2016 had sensors, microchips or data modems embedded.[5] This is encouraging, given the still fragmented relay technology for mobile data transmission. In the industrial sphere, there are now jet engines collecting information at 5,000 data points per second[6] and some aircraft carry as many as 20,000 data feelers in its wings.[7]

But such pioneering businesses have clearly preempted the emerging connected product era, set to comprise an estimated 200bn smart objects by 2020. Research shows that investment in cloud technology has now reached an average 14 percent of IT budgets, up from only five percent in 2011. Over 50 percent of enterprises' new IT spending will be on cloud-enabled technologies by 2018 according to IDC.[8]

Digitizing PLM End-to-End – the Main Challenge

As I said at the beginning of this chapter, the dawn of the connected or Living Product requires a changeover to new approaches in end-to-end PLM. Industrial manufacturers must restructure not only status quo engineering and manufacturing but service operation processes in order to gain the necessary agility and acceleration in cycle times as well as flexibility for customization.

A Leading Manufacturer of Construction, Mining and Power Generation Equipment Brings down Complexity in its Global PLM

A leading heavy equipment manufacturer had grown through takeovers. Meanwhile its Product Data Management (PDM) solutions had historically performed poorly. All this created a very complex multi-site PLM environment, with dozens of PDM anchors around legacy mainframe solutions for Bills of Materials (BOM) and part management.

The complex environment combined with the resulting process inefficiencies and data inaccuracies became a limiting factor in the company's ability to achieve their vision for "design anywhere, build anywhere," significant time-to-market improvements and improved order-to-delivery throughput. Furthermore, the cost to support, maintain and deliver new capabilities within the environment grew as the environment complexity grew.

To address the inefficiencies, a two-pronged effort was defined and executed. A multi-phase PLM transformation program focused on addressing key business challenges associated with the fragmented product development and data management environment was devised – to "link the End-to-End Bill-of-Materials flow".

A new global operating model for PLM service delivery – support, maintenance and new capability delivery – now drives operational excellence and cost savings – to "ensure efficient investments within PLM."

The PLM transformation program is expected to deliver hundreds of millions of dollars in annual benefits through improved global collaboration, reduced engineering changes and the elimination of "hidden factories" necessary to operate within the current environment.

Furthermore, improvements in the PLM environment are more effective due to the new PLM service delivery operating model, which has significantly lowered delivery costs, while increasing operational performance through new processes, tools and better skills alignment and flexibility.

The emergence of the Living Product also forces engineering departments to take on board and accommodate new skills, for instance, in software, data management and connectivity. All of a sudden these teams also have to work with completely new stakeholders such as end-customers and ecosystem partners. A good deal of cultural change is necessary.

How does one put adequate DPLM in place? At a general level, it works by using the advantages offered by interlinking data technology. This lets you weave an effective product development value network as shown in Figure 6.3. This network processes data circularly and is drastically different from the old mode of running PLM in a linear fashion from ideation to end-of-life retirement.

Figure 6.3 – Digital PLM Network[9]

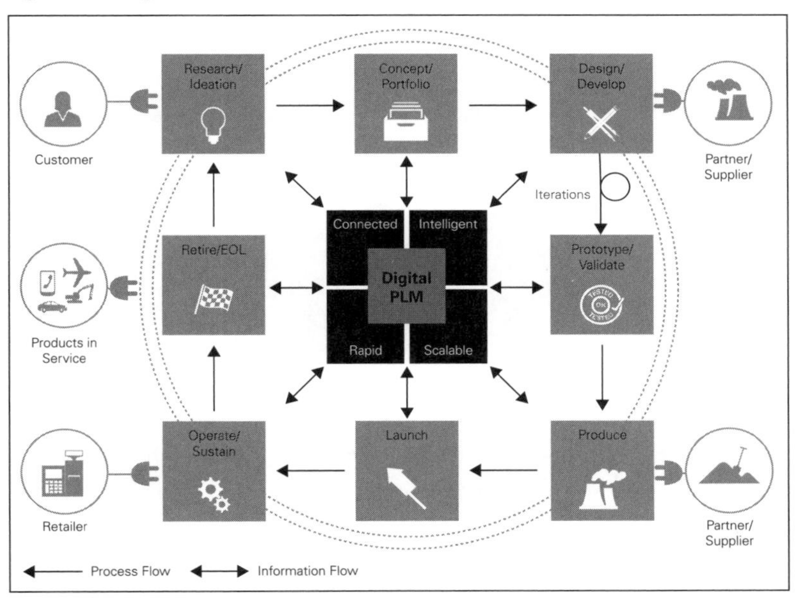

As the diagram shows, there are four things your PLM will need to be: rapid, scalable, intelligent and connected.

1. Rapid. In the Outcome Economy, you will need minimum response time between different enterprise functions. For instance, the faster concept evaluations can be fed through recurring design-prototype test loops, the faster they can be executed in the manufacturing function to fill an identified market gap with a high-margin product or service. Changing requirements sensed in the market, for instance via social media or crowdsourcing, should, within minutes, translate into the realization in R&D labs that product features need changing or that a different image profile is required in marketing.

Technology is always important in increasing agility. Simulation-led design using high-performance computing allows significantly acceleration of design and validations cycles. And rapid prototyping allows for a lean, iterative and agile approach for producing and refining products during the early design phases. Thus, product designs can be communicated and tested early with customers and collaborators and problems can also be found early in the design cycle, reducing scrap, rework or retooling.

3D Printing is a great example, making possible quick, cheap, one-off production of objects that would once only have been economical to mass-produce. In product development, this allows the very quick creation of high-definition prototypes.

Drone maker Aerialtronics used 3D Printing to drastically reduce lead times and cut its R&D time by about 50 percent while creating customizable Unmanned Aircraft Systems (UAS).[10] Using the same technology, Italian motorcycle maker Ducati has reduced engine design time from 28 months to eight,[11] while German automotive group BMW has deployed the technology to make highly adapted hand tools for workers that are 72 percent lighter.[12] Car manufacturer Honda also invested in rapid prototyping to accelerate product introduction and seek feedback on its designs.[13]

2. Scalable. This is the second most important trait of a powerful Digital PLM process and is closely related to the first. Usually in business when we talk about scalability, we mean the ability to expand an offering. In the Outcome Economy it will be about both expansion and contraction, the ability to quickly spot a demand and meet it, but also scale back at minimal loss as the demand recedes. Also, scalability is about improved product development efficiencies at lower costs.

In practice this can earn companies, according to some estimates, a 30 to 70 percent reduction in cost for managing a product. Some enterprises even reported a ten-fold improvement in workforce effectiveness.

US engineering conglomerate GE, for instance, has crowdsourced the design of a jet engine bracket via its DPLM and, through this, could save substantial weight. The company's traditional process for building a new jet engine often took two years, but can be greatly reduced through the use of 3D Printing.[14]

You should work towards conceptualizing, designing, testing and manufacturing a new product or service in quick succession, and ensure it can serve as a platform and container for continuous and fluid software updates and new service propositions. This forms the basis for scaling your product or service lines quickly, guided by the market's receptivity. For instance, automakers and industrial equipment manufacturers are using high performance computing to assess vastly more design options for transmissions while reducing the number of physical prototypes.

To get to mutiple release rollouts quickly, all functions involved must sing from the same hymn sheet, for which unfettered data flows across functions are important. Such a release pattern not only supports revenue growth, it also reduces R&D cost per unit, improving development efficiency.

This will also most often imply a complete revamp of the product's hardware features, software, and user interface. Just bolting on new features, services, and technology will not deliver scalability. You need ideally to completely reinvent the product concept. Of course, the concept of quick and agile scalability will take time to be introduced. It is even possible it will not make sense in some cases until an industrial manufacturing company really has embarked on managing daily product releases in the way Facebook or Amazon do today.

3. Intelligent. Your enterprise processes should command powerful analytics tools to filter out the exact product or service features needed in a certain phase of the market. In turn, connected products should be equipped with software that is smart enough to report relevant facts about usage trends and individual needs or preferences so R&D teams can respond accordingly. Software intelligence within PLM is the basis for getting connected products to the level of Living Products as it allows for permanent reinvention, reconfiguration, hyperpersonalization, and real-time adaptive user experience. A highly connected and software-intelligent PLM can also incorporate services from ecosystem partners to be included in your product and lengthen its lifespan. High-tech companies such as Apple have deployed unified ALM-PLM software allowing them to design to a single set of requirements across physical and digital components facilitating better outcomes and reduced time to market

4. Connected. This should hold together your whole PLM approach. There are many phases involved in a PLM scheme – from ideation, concept, design, prototype, validation, manufacturing, usage and support in the field straight through to the final retirement of a product. All these stages are best interlinked by uniform, unhindered, and, most importantly, integrated information and data flow.

Be aware that your business will eventually itself be embedded in an ecosystem of external suppliers, partners, sub-contractors and customers. To really benefit from all their immediate planning, knowledge, insights, and action and maximize the financial benefits for all parties, a pervasive data exchange mechanism is necessary at any given moment.

Seek to exploit digital data modeling to the maximum. Digital twins of physical products in the field will enable better operation of products. PLM systems today have the ability to create and manage digital twins throughout a product's lifecycle. These digital twin models are expected to be used extensively by manufacturing and service systems for predictive maintenance, repairs, design improvements etc. throughout the life of a product.

If these four basic features are heeded, your PLM should powerfully master the era of connected products. Your corporate functions will be nimble, swift and flexible enough to sense and adapt to changing customer needs and able to come up with products spanning both physical and digital value chains. They will be open and agile enough to allow customers, development partners, and suppliers to continually influence your strategy throughout the entire product lifecycle. They will be capable of harnessing the power of data, the most valuable internal and external currency of a digital enterprise. And you will remain in a permanent state of innovation, able to reach out at any given moment for the best means available to build successful new propositions for the market.

A Leading Tire Manufacturer Hit the Road Quicker and at Lower Cost

A leading tire manufacturer launched a digitally driven research acceleration scheme that cut its time to market in half and brought development cost down by a third.

This was the result of a program, which the company devised over three years, focusing on the restructuring of the R&D processes to achieve an agreed set of acceleration targets. Its own product mastery and production expertise was complemented by external support offering productive challenges to teams and systems. In close alignment, orthodoxies were questioned and new ideas and methodologies proposed.

A set of key performance indicators was also put in place, along with a result-driven mindset and innovation methodologies such as Quality Function Deployment for finding "the voice of the customer" as well as schemes such as Raw Material Design Event, Value Creation Office, and Human Dynamics. The company also got in touch with both global and local expertise for building an open ecosystem around its products.

The results of the R&D restructuring are a reduction of overall sell-out cost by over 30 percent and a shortening of the time to market from seven to three years.

The Stepped Road to Future-Proofed DPLM

So where does your business practice currently stand with regard to DPLM? If you can give positive answers to the following few questions, I would say your DPLM process already has the right foundations.

Are you using digital platforms such as social media, customer forums, and product and point-of-sale info to generate new concepts and product ideas or determine the end of a product life cycle? Are you also able to effectively measure cost and benefit so as to direct your product portfolio decisions? Do you have a data-based customer feedback mechanism or usage data helping you decide which product segment to grow, which to harvest and which to phase out? Do you have a strategy in place to exploit cloud technology or apply artificial intelligence in order to address development costs or speed-to-market targets? Do you already use digital platforms to simulate or validate products, collaborate with suppliers, capture product performance or analyze market or sales data?

Figure 6.4 – Leveraging Technology in R&D[15]

R&D

Foundation Technology	Strategy	Discover	Execute	Operate
Connected Devices	Open Innovation Platforms Innovation Management Tools	Usage, Performance Data, Expansion of Products to Services	Demand Sensing Integrated Real-Time Development Progress Monitoring	Early User Insights Based on Real-Time Usage Data, Product Updates, Vendor Collaboration
Social	Social Listening/ Market Insights Digital Focus Groups	Connected Customer Consumer-Centric Insights, Social-Based OI & Listening	Targeted Product Testing	Continuous Customer Feedback Insights Based on Real-Time Usage Data
Mobile		Application Development, Integration, Real-Time Feedback, and Crowdsourcing	Product Offering Testing	Real-Time Consumer Feedback
Cloud	Insights and Analytics Platform	Usage, Performance Data, Expansion of Products to Services	Monitoring & Diagnostics, Predictive Maintenance, Asset Lifecycle	Early User Insights Based on Real-Time Usage Data, Product Updates, Vendor Collaboration
Digital	Concept Finalization	Closed-Loop Feedback	Sustainability and Quality into Product Design	Improved Sourcing Based on Real-Time Product Feedback
3D Scanning/ Printing	Digital Printing	Virtual Modeling and Simulations	Physical Test Digital Prototyping (3D Printing)	
Automated Assistance		System Engineering Tools & Architecture	Robotics Programming "as Designed"	Remote Monitoring Technical Publication Tools
Analytics/ Artificial Intelligence	Predictive Marketing/ Sales Analytics Predictive Segmentation Analytics Predictive Social Media Analytics	Real-Time Business Decisions Based on R&D Analytics Ideation & Customer Collaboration	Supplier Quality Analysis	Customer Profitability Analysis Warranty Analytics
Virtual Reality		Virtual Consumer Environment	Experimenting, Virtual Prototyping/Simulation Testing	
Cyber Security	Strengthen Customer Relationships, Reduce Business Risks Through Security, Data Privacy and Ethics			

Digital Product Lifecycle Management – Accenture Lets You Match Markets Faster

Digital Product Lifecycle Management (DPLM) is an integral end-to-end concept radically departing from conventional corporate thinking. It creates an opportunity for manufacturers to completely re-think the way they produce products and services and the associated processes, workforce and customer engagements.

DPLM-managed products will be designed, prototyped, manufactured, assembled, distributed, and operated in digitally driven ultra-automated lifecycles so that they can be introduced at unprecedented speed and scale.

To achieve end-to-end digital transformation, DPLM embodies the combination effect of a wide range of technologies including artificial intelligence (AI), always-connected advanced sensors, real-time analytics, augmented mixed and virtual reality, generative design and part consolidation, crowdsourcing, 3D Printing and ultra-postponement, edge intelligence, Blockchain, social media, flexible film-like electronic circuits, and the entire spectrum of autonomous robotics.

Consumer inputs and market trends are incorporated early and often to ensure that products and services are introduced and adaptable to market needs. Customer inclusion during the whole process becomes a differentiating advantage.

The industrial workforce will be highly collaborative and connected, and augmented to accelerate the way they manage tasks and learn new skills.

Acceptance-at-scale will be driven by an analysis-driven workforce that can complete tasks in rapidly reduced time cycles. Equipped with technologies like mixed reality to visualize products and processes and AI to complete tedious tasks, the workforce will benefit hugely. Product engineers will use fully immersive experiences like virtual reality to design products, and then be able

Figure 6.5 – The Digital Product Lifecycle's Combination Effect[16]

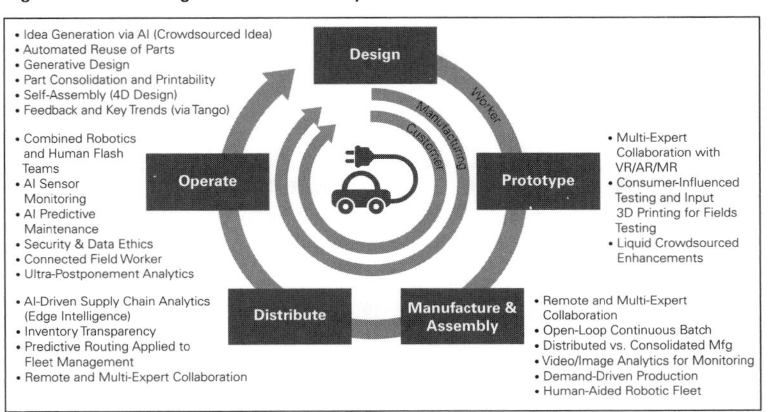

to immediately simulate in-field performance to discover design enhancements. Remote collaboration with colleagues and even external teams will provide richer and greater insight for creating new products.

Within the entire product lifecycle, three key areas will be most impacted: engineering, production and operation. In product engineering, for example, the use of digital product twins allows engineers to visualize, prototype, simulate and test products before they are built. A product can be simulated in a large number of real-world scenarios rather than specific pre-defined circumstances, resulting in better products developed in far fewer iterations.

Accenture is investing R&D capital in the three aspects of Industry X.0 that will change the way businesses create, produce and operate products: the processes, the associated workforce, and the customers.

	Design	Make	Service
Pro-cesses	• Agile, short and fast iteration of product development (fail-fast approach) • Highly automated and augmented through the use of advanced AI techniques	• Optimization of parts (minimize the number while increase quality) • Optimization of the overall product to create highly configurable and adaptive intelligent products • Optimization of location of production and overall supply-chain logistics with real-time information	• Real-time tracking of product usage, customer's needs • Self-configuration and adaptation based on customer's needs • Identification and anticipation of future needs (products and services) • Good integration with a platform to deliver services in real-time
Human Work-force	• Collaborative • Crowd-enabled • Highly augmented (e.g., with wearables and real-time information)	• Dynamic scheduling, staffing and sourcing • On-demand augmented training • Orchestration of a wide range of work involving both humans and robots	• Remote monitoring, diagnosis, and repair • Orchestration of services across multiple organizations
Cus-tomer	• Incorporation of customer feedback and market trend early and often in the life cycle • Co-innovation with key customers – in-cluding early pilot and deployment	• Delivery of products and services at the point and time required (e.g., 3D Printing) • Traceability of parts throughout the supply chain	• Intelligent anticipation of customer needs and delivery of the right services at the right time. • Capture of feedback on unmet needs incorporated into future products and services

Digital PLM already Generates Value for Real Businesses

Transforming your DPLM is a necessity if you are to cope with the transformation of legacy products into Living Products and the introduction of new digital technologies to your existing product development processes, allowing you to achieve new levels of efficiency. Implementing these new technologies leads to significantly shorter development cycles, development budgets and manufacturing costs in the range of 40 percent.

A lot has to change, but this is worthwhile. A simulation shows that the deployment of DPLM will bring $100m-$150m incremental EBITDA improvement per annum from sales of $25bn in a typical industrial company.

There are some intriguing examples of where DPLM is already productively used.

Understanding usage via connected products allows one to enrich customer experiences. By gathering and analyzing data for each truck deployed at a work site, service teams at heavy equipment makers such as Caterpillar are able to advise customers on optimizing their fleet. The electric carmaker Tesla, meanwhile, uses remote-controlled software updates to keep its fleet up-to-date with the newest technology.[17]

DPLM can also hugely widen the scope of R&D and design by bringing in outsiders, including end-users. Computer maker Dell created a collaboration platform, IdeaStorm, for ideation and real-time product portfolio management. It provided a digital toolbox for would-be inventors, gathering 24,000 ideas of which 550 have been implemented.[18] Similarly, French arms maker DCNS uses virtual reality and so-called mixed immersive environments to allow customers to experience the product at various stages of development.[19]

Finally, there are the gains in communication within organizations. For instance, an aerospace and defense manufacturer uses wearables to remotely access products. Employees at a work item transmit pictures via software-enabled glasses to experts for consultation. Industrial manufacturers such as Hyundai offer mobile apps to package managers so they can access status and design information and update and enrich data workflow tasks.

A useful overview of how to develop your very own tailored PLM process is offered in the table below (Figure 6.6). It gives a good indication of when to trigger the next step in digital development, depending on how fast your target market is likely to move to the Outcome Economy.

Figure 6.6 – Digital PLM Roadmap[20]

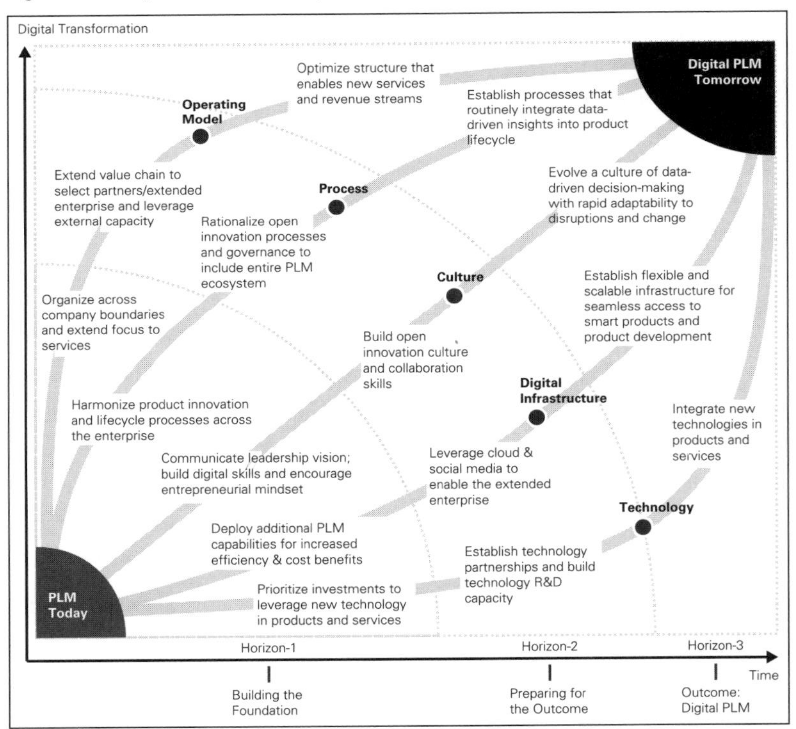

Such a roadmap to an ideal PLM could come in handy for many industrial manufacturers. Research data shows that while just under a third of executives are "very satisfied" with their performance in converting ideas into market-ready products, services, or business models, only 21 percent feel they have an effective process for "capturing ideas from outside their company" and 28 percent cite "lateness to market" as a key reason for innovation failure.[21]

Choose the Right Speed for Changing Processes and People

With a proper PLM road map in place one can start to think about building effective product development processes practicable in an era of outcome-oriented customers and connected products.

Note, in particular, that as you embark on digital product development, all your activities in that segment of the value chain must be at least as data-intelligent, responsive, agile and complex as the products they aim to conceive.

For such development processes to work, much more permeability is needed between hitherto siloed functions and units, from supply chain management right through to aftersales and customer support. At many points in the process, entirely new communication lines and so far uncharted micro-processes are needed, as are the idea inputs and actions of new people and software components.

In practice, the transition is further complicated by the fact that your old and new world must be kept operational under one enterprise roof. All of a sudden, blueprints for "dumb" legacy products commanding still high market traction, must be complemented by designs of entirely new offerings with demonstrable service utility beyond mere mechanical function. Moving the old and the New forward in tandem is not easy.

For product engineers and product designers, the awkward transition phase will require "living hybrids," legacy products that take on more and more software intelligence. Eventually, the increasing service character of industrial goods will force developers to look into a kaleidoscope of entirely new customer propositions if they want to keep their employer profitable and grow both top and bottom line. This requires the right management processes and a team with the right training, skill and creativity. New experts in digital product development may need to be hired, but even they will be in a new world.

The end-to-end flow of relevant data will provide higher resolution information about what teams do and where. Generally, in a fully fledged digital development process, a lot more data will be produced and handled than in conventional approaches. New information will be produced every time a development engineer defines a new product feature, a software expert scribbles a solution for a specific problem or an additional component is selected for manufacturing. Terabytes of data will be amassed, rehashed and filtered daily to make sure it is available to all personnel relevant to a development process.

All this clearly poses risks. Development process digitization could remain half-baked, weakening creativity and team discipline and creating additional cost. Or your newly introduced R&D data handling and DPLM could fail completely. The development process could become suffocated under too much irrelevant, poorly sifted data flowing through design suites, engineering and prototyping departments.

A key risk, easy to overlook, is staff failing to keep up with the technological great leap forward. Old-world development teams with plenty of pre-digital R&D experience will have to immerse themselves in this ecosystem and digest a huge amount of information from the market and many other sources. This is probably the most daunting pain point in their departure from an unconnected product development practice.

Only a short while ago many companies had just moved from blueprints, stencils and clay models to 3D digital representation of products and prototypes. Now, in today's digital vanguard sectors such as automotive, products move from idea generation to concept stage to detailed design to test launch, adjustment and post-launch on one single, uninterrupted data conveyor belt, broadening as it passes through each phase.

Catching up too quickly with this advanced world could cause problems for laggard companies as new processes and people have no time to really combine productively. I will discuss how to manage this in much greater detail in the next chapter.

Electronics and High-Tech Pointing the Way for Industry

To get a sense of how all this should work, let's look at development of a new mobile phone. Here, DPLM is effectively already in place. All manufacturers, from Apple to HTC, now progress from idea generation to launch and eventually to retirement exclusively through digital formats.

The project teams start by envisaging what a defined target customer wants and how this primary information should be effectively cascaded into the digital development process. This preliminary stage is about deciding raw parameters like size, quality levels or general performance. This would also include a first step at defining functionalities – how many cameras, screen resolution, whether to make the SIM card electronic – and the phone's packaging and support materials such as mains adaptors in short every aspect of the product.

To get the development process rolling, the requirements need to be passed on to the designers and development engineers, the mechanical group, the electrical group and the teams further down the line that will give the device more detailed design shape, where features such as screen size, number of app symbols displayed and what casing is used are concretely defined. In this way the whole development process rolls on swiftly, with effective sharing of digital information from stage to stage and detail to detail.

Although all these different teams work on their different options and choices, the overarching mechanism is clear: digitally conveyed planning, designing and engineering is much more precise and fast and mutual reaction loops to each team's actions are dramatically minimized.

In the end, once all features and functionalities are defined, you have to test them all and adjust them if necessary. Here again a plethora of looping data flows will form complex individual tasks and decisions. In order to remain quick, agile and responsive, this is best done on one comprehensive and integrated digital development platform routing data to reach people who must know how to put it to productive use.

A phone is obviously a complex product requiring orchestrated input from multiple business support functions. Clearly, the more relevant data is circulated among decision-makers to facilitate coordinated decision-making, the better the phone's chance of becoming popular with consumers. This is only possible with a fully digitized development process.

Mobile Phone Functionality Gives Manufacturers a Major Steer

Early mobile phones ran on release cycles typically measured in years. Over time, and with consequences for those that could not keep up, this has reduced to months, now with an established consumer expectation of significant upgrades happening within the year, and smaller increments even faster.

From that perspective smartphones can so far be seen as the most connected products in industrial history. No other mass-scale product can be so well studied and monitored in the field after it has left production. This is possible because of its high software content and connectedness as well as its quality as a platform product – that is, a product that serves as a platform for third-party applications.

These apps, much more than the phone's hardware, overwhelmingly define the user experience. That also sets the direction for the developer and design team. This is perhaps the key way in which smartphones point towards the future for so many other consumer and business products that currently contain much less connectivity.

This is not simply a matter of providing a blank slate for apps. Apple's engineers and UX (user experience) designers make platform decisions that enable certain app functionality. They have, for instance, built an accelerometer into the iPhone so the device knows which way you are holding it. This platform hardware enables numerous user apps including step counters or gauges of g-force for car drivers. In the same vein, elementary geo-positioning technology such as GPS is installed as the launch pad for navigational services taking shape in various apps from Google Maps to local pizza delivery services. In this regard, smartphones have definitely reached the Open Innovation platform status many other products will only achieve many years down the line.

True, Apple and Google still decide which apps go into their digital stores for download. But the platform character of their hardware and operating systems potentially turn any user able to write a few lines of code into a digital developer for one big crowd-based development process that has long left the factory gates behind.

For industrial sectors, similar initiatives have already been launched. Big industrial equipment producers such as Germany's Siemens have created software platforms such as MindSphere for the machinery they sell. This is modeled after the iPhone in that end-users of industrial machinery can use these platforms to develop their own applications and software analytics products tailored precisely to their needs.

The Problem of Beating the Clock – How and Which One of the Many?

Many industrial sectors are, of course, much less advanced than phone makers and are still struggling with a hurdle that the iPhone long ago cleared: the growing speed at which hardware and software innovation cycles diverge.

Cars are a good example. A new model – not just a revamp, but a new vehicle version in its own right – is designed to last around five to seven years. This is typical of car production platforms because, unlike phone manufacturing, they are still capital-intensive and need a minimum timespan to return investment. The clock can hardly go faster. The technological concept is designed to be up-to-date for a defined time during which features like its engine, gear box or central locking mechanism will be considered contemporary and attractive buyer propositions. Development engineers look at this model more or less as a static object during this period, coming off the production line in thousands of identical copies.

A Car Manufacturer Overcomes the Hurdles to Establish Systems Engineering

A leading global automotive group recognized the need to transform their product development operations due to increasing product complexity and compressed development cycles.

The original equipment manufacturer (OEM) faced challenges in collaboration across functions during product development, leading to late discovery of failure modes, high rework for design elements that crossed organizational boundaries, and lower overall design efficiency and effectiveness.

The legacy organization was structured and operated in a way that siloed collaboration and development within functions. Collaboration across functions was informal and not aligned to individual metrics and incentives.

Systems Engineering, which uses systems thinking to coordinate teams, functions, skills and knowledge, offered a possible solution. The group recognized this, but didn't have a clear path to align stakeholders and deploy the methodology.

Throughout more than 12 of its organizations, leadership across functions and organizations was engaged to develop a common understanding of the target state and the challenges and road-blocks to deployment. Function-specific and organization-wide solutions and recommendations were developed to address priority challenges and hurdles to adoption. These were iterated with leadership from each function to encourage buy-in.

To accelerate adoption, a 100-day plan was developed to galvanize the organization in quickly defining key Systems Engineering operating model elements required to test the methodology's disciplines on vehicle program pilots.

The aim was for pilots to target specific value capture that would demonstrate the discipline's benefit across functions and increase product development effectiveness and efficiency. To this end, key process, asset, organizational and system requirements were defined and key system, process, governance, metric and strategy initiatives and capabilities were implemented.

This plan formed the starting point for learning from the pilots and scaling beyond them, taking Systems Engineering to full implementation on new vehicle programs in 18 months.

The problem is the software that increasingly imbues such a product: features such as a satnav, predictive maintenance, mobility guarantees, and digital ignition controls that update frequently. Software lifecycles in car manufacturing are only one or two years long. This clock cannot be slowed to match the hardware.

Neither the car manufacturers nor its customers want a young software heart beating in a dated physical body. It would be much more desirable to give a cutting-edge software heart a fluidly changing hardware shell. Since this is impossible, the art is to synchronize the two clocks.

This is why you need digitally fluid design and development processes. Agility in overall design for hardware and software allows for a better, although not complete, synchronization of the two clocks. Where synchronization is impossible, because of high cost, software updates can at least "modernize" a driver's experience by augmenting the aging hardware body. This is where software-enabled user interface design shows its importance.

The economic fallout from shortening the hardware cycle in order to get it closer to the software cycle can be significant. The production platform for a physical product with only a three-year market lifespan has to turn out much higher volumes to make the investment profitable. Often the end-user market is too small for this. In this case, it might be better to work with a platform solution for the physical casing with short-term upgrade flexibility in some features of the hardware and also keep the software application update cycle really short. This could eventually bring both cycles into closer step.

You can, for instance, handle two different clock speeds in one product by designing your hardware without permanently wiring in electronic parts. That allows software cycles greater independence from each other in terms of the hardware they require.

In the B2B sector this may be even more important than in B2C. For example, increasingly, industrial equipment makers are embracing these technologies. Their tractors, cranes and bulldozers are such major investments that buyers demand regular software updates with minimum hassle. That is only doable when hardware is not "hard-plumbed" in.

There are, by the way, more clocks to keep an eye on. A third clock, outside hardware and software, is the one behind the user interface, which determines the user experience. It similarly has to be synchronized within your product lifecycle and it can be a tricky task as hardware products such as cars start operating more and more like a platform for which you will be expected to provide new apps on a weekly basis.

US car manufacturer Tesla can, at any time, provide their fleet on the road with the latest versions of its semi-autonomous driving algorithms, maps and battery control applications. This happens automatically and as simply as upgrades to a laptop's operating system.

Of course, Tesla has the big advantage of having created their car platform very recently. They had no legacy markets to observe, so were able to take hardware and application lifecycles into full account from day one, building R&D processes around them. Conventional unconnected cars are much more cumbersome, much more locked into hard-won hardware engineering solutions. You have to report to dealers to update software. Electronic parts sometimes have to be replaced.

My reckoning is that consumers and B2B clients alike will realistically accept hardware cycles of around two years as long as they receive regular software updates – in the same way they accept a three-year-old computer, as long as it runs the most recent operating system. Many customers might even stick deliberately to an older hardware version they like.

Takeaways

1. The entire process chain around developing and designing industrially manufactured items is redefined by the emergence of the smart and connected product.
2. Strengthen your software capabilities. There will be more and more software embedded in your products. Software-enabled services and user experience will be critical, you need to build at pace your software capabilities.
3. A robust Digital Product Lifecycle Management (DPLM) must be the starting point for product development in the emerging era of data-driven Living Products. Set up the right DPLM capabilities: agility, scalability, software intelligence, and unified data connectedness.
4. Synchronize, but do not lock together, the two clocks – and ensure that marketing optimizes the resulting propositions and improvements with regard to the customer.
5. End-to-end. Let your DPLM run through your whole business and become its DNA.

07

Chapter 7

Zoom in: How to Create a Connected Industrial Workforce

The future's connected industrial worker will be a highly productive, data-based decision-maker and supervisory presence – on the factory floor, in engineering centers, and in boardrooms. She or he will leverage analytics, collaborate with robots, and be protected by safety and tracking technology. Far from science fiction's human vs. machine conflicts, the new shop floors will host a blended workforce, humans and machines jointly delivering outcomes neither could produce alone. Importantly, in the many sectors where automation holds sway, most of those humans will be white-collar workers. Essentially, the bulk of today's blue-collar roles will turn into more white-collar, supervisory positions, while the remainder will ultimately be automated away. Enterprises will therefore experience significant workforce transformation and they will need to adopt a more active role in training and developing staff, including supporting managers in stepping up to their new change agent role.

The digital transformation of industrial manufacturing means a huge increase in software-intelligent, autonomous machines and products. Devices such as wearable computers, software controlled eye-glasses, smart watches, digital wristbands, handheld accessories like smartphones or touchpads, and ubiquitous wireless connectivity and search capacity will soon allow humans, machines and algorithms not only to coexist but truly collaborate.

This critical joining of two types of operational "thinkers" is a first in industrial history. It will, as time progresses, bring about a complete merger of remits, tasks and planning across humans and machines.

Science fiction's dehumanized future dystopias turn out to be a false prediction. Human ability will not be supplanted by machine capacity, it will be complemented by it. In fact, there will a multitude of new jobs for humans, many of them more stimulating than those from manufacturing's past. What's more, future work set-up designers will serve a workforce of digital natives, people who have grown up with computers and feel comfortable with them. To best serve them, designers may even offer work interfaces to mimic the game designs many of them love.

Robot technologies have reached a watershed on this journey. They are now clever, convenient, safe, and flexible enough to be inserted into human workflows. They "augment" a workforce's activities, providing more efficiency, productivity and value. They can sense, understand and quickly adapt to their environment, enabling them to interact in human style with real people to create a hybrid human-robot workflow.

The rapid progress of digital technology, including software and machine learning, sensors and analytic tools, drives this steadily emerging union of man and machine. In this way a digitally connected industrial workforce is created that operates in highly efficient, versatile and responsive workplaces – a reality that will strongly contrast with many of today's standards on industrial factory floors.

The primary objectives of the human-digital recombination are to gain value-creating efficiency and productivity by multiplying the effects of human physical and cognitive power and enabling managers and employees to make better judgments. This will reshape industrial production and service design in the name of future outcome-based value creation.

Figure 7.1 shows what business executives from various industry sectors expect from the successive blending of their human workforces with machines across various functions. In a recent study, 925 business leaders in Australia, Brazil, China, India, Japan, the United States and the European Union were interviewed to understand how business leaders and policy makers can use digital technologies to accelerate growth and competitiveness. As you can see, gains in productivity, innovation, cost efficiencies and agility achieved the highest scores, with quality of work, employee engagement and safety following not far behind.

Figure 7.1 – Top Organizational Benefits from Adopting Digital Technologies[1]

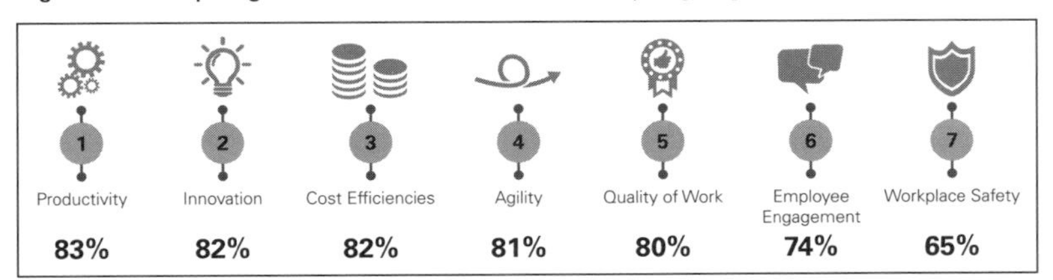

The blended human-machine environment will indeed yield tremendous economic advantages. By 2020 a fully connected workforce can unlock a further €250m in profit for a car manufacturer with annual revenues of €25bn.[2] For a typical industrial manufacturer, the potential is precisely the same but with much more coming from functions such as R&D and product support than from manufacturing which is still the premier pool of value to tap for carmakers.

Mutuality Between Humans and Machines Across the Whole Enterprise

Next to extra value, the blurring of borders between the minds of workers, managers, machines and products will also trigger the introduction of entirely new work practices across the industrial sector. It is fair to say that *all* business roles and functions will be affected. Outcomes, approaches, experiences and routines on shop floors, in back offices, in R&D, and in boardrooms are going to be altered significantly.

At first, digital technology will augment humans, and then progressively shift toward humans augmenting machines. On the one hand, humanoid, collaborative machine thinking will push human thinking and actions. On the other, robots will also be augmented by human programming or by their own algorithmic observations of human thinking and actions. Robots will already be colleagues, or, as experts like to say, "cobots," but the final control and decision-making will still lie with human workers and managers able to override machine reasoning.

The technological substrate for this will be ubiquitous digital data. Streams of information will be pumped through industrial enterprises as physical and virtual sensors systematically detect and recollect internal work streams and external events in a company's wider ecosystem. With high-capacity, cloud-based server networks, it will be possible to process and store these gigantic data throughputs and keep them operational for the connected workforce.

Advanced data analytics and modelling, for example, will transform data into insights for decisions at all enterprise levels and in all functions and roles. Algorithms will automatically discover which process variations have resulted in higher performance so that they can be replicated elsewhere in the value chain. And product designs at intermediate development stage are going to be digitally represented, saving cost in prototyping and testing.

Large circulated data loads will be able to improve human productivity in at least two key ways. First, they will be able to foster workers' cognitive input into a process by freeing up their headspace for other more value-creating tasks. Second, routine activities will be able to be left to robotic co-workers thanks to voice recognition, natural language processing, and other technological advances.

But data technologies can also improve the ways in which employees touch base, coordinate and co-create new products and services – for instance, by enabling social networking, discussion groups, online file-sharing, real-time videoconferencing, and task and project management using virtual, augmented, or mixed reality. Human workers will, for instance, be able to project themselves into a wide variety of situations through remotely controlled avatars so that they can collaborate, as a research and development team, from various locations on a generative design project.

Low-Supervision Shop-Floor Machine-Centricity – It's Nearly Here

I said above that at first human enterprise roles would not be replaced. However, in just a few years largely manual, labour-based environments will be transformed by the broad use of autonomous machines with minimally invasive human supervision over practically unmanned shop floors. At this point, new human jobs will take on greater importance.

Figure 7.2, representing the findings from a survey of business leaders on the rate of technological change on their shop floors, lays out the stages of this journey, and gives a good indication of the rate of change.

Figure 7.2 – Augmentation-Automation Spectrum[3]

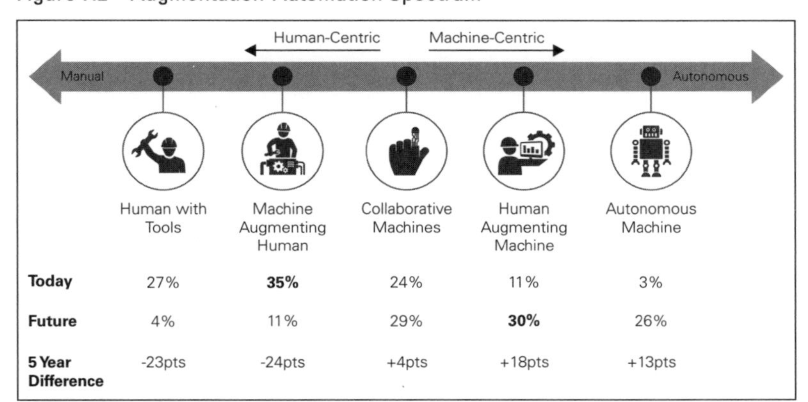

	Human with Tools	Machine Augmenting Human	Collaborative Machines	Human Augmenting Machine	Autonomous Machine
Today	27%	**35%**	24%	11%	3%
Future	4%	11%	29%	**30%**	26%
5 Year Difference	-23pts	-24pts	+4pts	+18pts	+13pts

The crucial findings are the figures in bold. These are the highest proportion of responses on where enterprises think they are right now versus where they expect to be in five years.

So the highest proportion of business leaders (35 percent) currently put their businesses in the category of "machines augmenting humans." A smaller but still significant number (27 percent) see themselves in the preceding "human with tool" stage, whereas, conversely, a similar proportion (24 percent) reports mature human-machine-collaboration in place on their factory floors.

Most businesses (30 percent) reckon that in five years time they will have arrived at the "human augmenting machine" stage, with similar proportions saying they expect to have reached "collaborative machine" or even "autonomous machine" levels by then.

Overall I expect that within the next five years, 96 percent of the workforce on industrial shop floors will be connected. By then we will see the critical shift from human-centric to machine-centric where today´s 62 percent human-centricity will have transformed into 52 percent machine-centricity.[4]

The Path to Collaborative Robots Running Enterprises

It is worth detailing the different phases of the process just described in order to better understand what businesses actually expect to happen.

We start at what is today's standard practice: humans using unconnected but advanced mechanical tools. This phase is followed by a period where tools become intelligent enough to augment humans, being able to carry out micro-tasks autonomously.

To give a very simple example, think of a hand-operated "dumb" screwdriver replaced by an electric power driver with automatic depth stop. This is a smartened tool taking over a task from humans – preventing screws from going in too deep. The productivity gains from this kind of augmentation are palpable: more screws set in a shorter time and with greater precision. Higher quality is achieved and less corrective work is required.

A proof of concept produced for a company of the aerospace and defense sector provides a more complex real-life enterprise analogy. Using contextual marking instructions, smart glasses worn by workers displayed all the information needed to mark the floor for seat positions. A worker wearing the glasses was able to act six times faster and reduce marking errors to zero.[5] The use of the glasses also improved workers' moods. They reported feeling more at ease and said the work environment felt greatly improved.

This is an example of human augmentation by machines. In a further step, it will eventually be supplanted by real collaboration between human and machine. How might this look in our screwdriver example?

It could entail a real company set-up in which an intelligent screwdriving robot – a cobot – when it senses a human co-worker instructing another robot to prepare components for assembly, would autonomously respond by equipping itself with the appropriate screws.

The degree to which such collaborative robot systems for shop floors have already advanced is demonstrated by industrial engineering company ABB where robots called YuMi have been specifically designed to completely remove barriers between human and machine on production lines. These robots no longer need humans with programming skills to operate them. They are programmed to act intuitively depending on their job.[6]

According to the business leaders we talked to, injection molding is the task most commonly assigned to cobots on today´s shop floors, with gluing and welding set to take over in the next five years. These leaders see the highest potential for collaborative robots, however, in general industrial assembly. One in three enterprises plan to assign this task to collaborating machines.

Among new tools, robots are seen as offering the greatest potential for efficiency gains, followed by other technologies such as automated vehicles or augmenting tools such as smart glasses and helmets (see Figure 7.3).

Figure 7.3 – Top Five Benefits Expected from Technologies/Devices in Manufacturing[7]

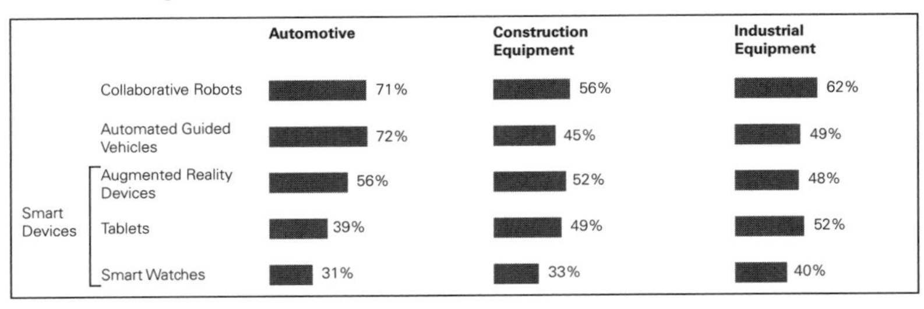

Yet even this stage of mechanical semi-intelligence will eventually be overridden by a technologically more advanced phase where human workers will augment machines rather then the other way round. Workers and engineers will, for instance, show a robot a certain task – welding two pieces of metal or gluing together plastic components – and then leave it to the machine's planning and implementing capacities to repeat this newly acquired, highly individualized skill on a series of other tasks.

At an even more advanced level, machine-centricity will set in. That means that cobots will become obsolete altogether, as machines become able to fully coordinate themselves on their own, sensing and carrying out the most complex tasks with minimal intervention by human controllers.

This stage, though it still sounds far-fetched, is already, in a limited way, a reality. German engineering specialist Siemens has recently started a so called "lights out" production plant, unmanned at factory floor level but remotely backed up by around 1,150 software programmers, engineers and support personnel.[8] At such an advanced level, the human workforce is not obsolete, but has left the shop floor. Its skill profile is now markedly different, not that of the blue-collar manual worker, but the skilled white-collar strategist or supervisor.

A Fully Connected Workforce Needs New Organizational Structures

As I say, business practitioners understand all the need for this dramatic change. Nevertheless, corresponding action is still thin on the ground.

The reassuring news is, only a tiny residual of businesses – six percent – say that a connected workforce is not yet essential to their business strategy. 85 percent see the evolution from human-centric to machine-centric manufacturing coming to their shop floors as early as 2020.[9]

Only 22 percent have so far implemented measures to accommodate these new work set-ups, but 18 percent of R&D budgets are already exclusively earmarked for investment in human-machine work blending, a figure poised to rise to 24 percent in 2020.[10]

We found that companies leading in digitization, such as those in the telecoms sector, already exhibit significant connected workforce solutions. This was especially true of businesses with a workforce of 10,000 or more. They also have strong action plans for rearranged processes and higher investments in the necessary technology. Sixty-three percent of these businesses say they already employ cobots in one form or another.

Our research also suggests that realizing the highly connected workforce requires deep organizational shifts, with changes crosscutting skills, roles and, importantly, overall enterprise cultures and lines of communication.

The control over information and decision-making has up to now been the domain of gate-keeping authorities at the center of organizations. It is about to be devolved and federalized. In the age of high data availability, company-wide connected workforces, and omnipresent connectivity in general, centralized decision-making will no longer make sense. Throughout a business the digital connections between systems, machines, sites, people and products will produce a dynamic flow of information about the whereabouts and concrete activity of all individual inputs. Local thinking and acting on the fringes will increasingly be the natural response. Workers will routinely combine data streams with their local contextual knowledge to make significant decisions on their own – for example about inventory stock, materials handling and even pricing or product design.

Of course, fringe actions will still be communicated to all other necessary operational points – perhaps even more efficiently, thanks to connectivity. The remainder of the organization will see and understand these independent moves and, where necessary, replicate them, accommodate them or override them.

All this will be enormously more efficient. Being transparent and having open lines of enterprise communication clearly already bolsters performance. Research by ClearCompany shows that businesses today with high levels of engaging communication among staff reported 22 percent greater productivity and 50 percent lower staff turnover relative to peers.[11]

In the fast-paced, real-time, demand-driven Outcome Economy, the gains will be even greater. The more empowered, connected workforce will allow companies to precisely respond to changing market conditions. Backed by intelligent processes, businesses, much more than just reacting, will be able to anticipate or even exploit change to achieve unprecedented outcomes while minimizing financial risk.

It is crucial to note that this local decision-making will, over all, increase worker skills and engagement. Beyond shop floors, digital technologies will also make design teams, marketing units, supply chains and boardrooms respond to changing market conditions in real-time.

Enterprises must prepare for this, providing workers at all levels with the data and skills needed to make sound business decisions. As our survey shows, only 32 percent of companies have thought about this.[12] It is imperative that they act very strategically, making sure the right people are paired with the right tools and skills in the right way.

Connected Workers Must Iterate, Adapt, and be Flexible

So, what does a viable talent mix look like for an ever more connected workforce?

Workers and managers alike will need a pronounced ability to learn and adapt. They should be trained to be better at autonomous judgement and action and at collaboration. It is no surprise, that social skills such as mentoring, persuading teams and emotional intelligence are among those most often cited as necessary in digital companies. Narrow-focused technical expertise is, notably, in significantly less demand.

Furthermore, digital environments require much more flexibility and speed in thinking and acting than analogue environments. Every single member of a connected workforce needs a deep-rooted motivation to process unprecedented information loads, draw conclusions from them and apply that knowledge to shape their remit. Ironically, the strengths that may have made people and organizations highly successful in the past could be the same ones that now hinder them in the fast-moving, agile world of digital.

The ability to work by modes of iteration, adaptation and even experimentation should be an important capability. Connected workers – white-collar as well as blue-collar – will need a much higher level of comfort with ambiguity and uncertainty and a willingness to move in the absence of complete agreement. It will also be necessary to replace legacy corporate paradigms that emphasize upfront planning with the ability to re-plan frequently in response to new data and changing conditions.

Figure 7.4. – Creating a Digital Culture in the Enterprise[13]

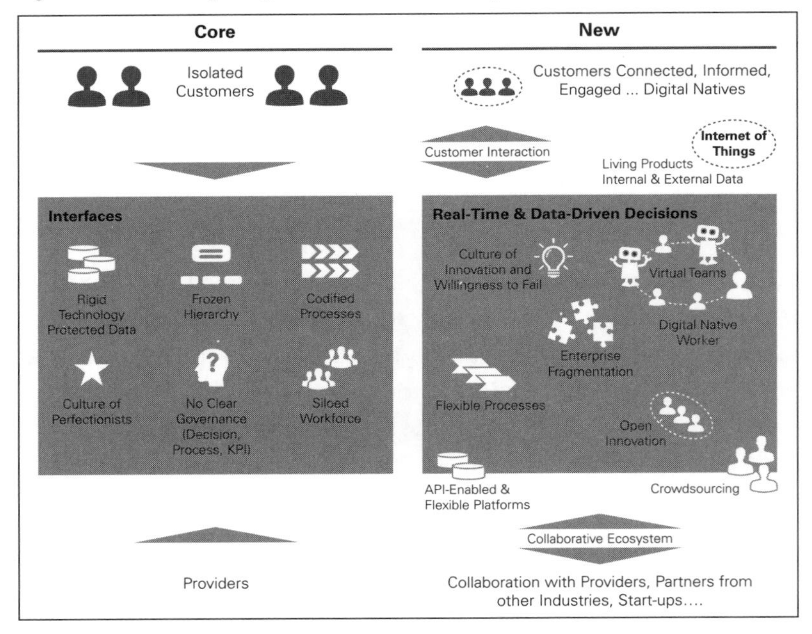

Crucially, especially in relation to the transition to digital, management skills will change. Top managers will need to understand the digital stakes for the company and its transformational needs. They must build and share a common vision accordingly, advocate for the transformation and identify the impacts on the organization.

They will also require a knack for numeracy to help connected employees make the most of available data.

Over all, manager minds will need to be much more fluid and adaptive. With silos and hierarchies collapsing in new organizational architectures, they will need to be collaborative with machines and other humans and agile at spotting gaps in the market in real-time and arranging digital processes accordingly.

They will need to phase out tight control and vertical instruction and introduce autonomy to foster creative idea generation throughout an enterprise's lower levels. They will need to inspire their teams and enable them to succeed. They will need to learn how to interpret analyses and recommendations provided by machines, to ask the right questions and improve decision-making. And they will need to develop, coach and collaborate with others on experimentation and innovation drives across the organization.

The Skills Managers Need to Succeed

While managers recognize the value of judgment work, they exhibit a blind spot for interpersonal skills – distinctly human qualities that will help to set them apart from AI in the workplace. The percentage of managers who placed the relevant skills as the top three needed to succeed in their role in five years' time:

Digital/Technology	42%
Creative thinking/Experimentation	33%
Data Analysis and Interpretation	31%
Strategy Development	30%
Planning and Administration	23%
Social Networking	21%

People Development and Coaching	21%
Collaboration	20%
Quality Management and Standards	20%
Sharpen Skills Within my Current Domain of Expertise	20%
Performance Management and Reporting	17%

Managerial Trust Issues Around Machines

Our empirical findings gathered in surveys suggest a paradox among respondents, though. On the one hand, 84 percent of managers at all levels believe machines will make them more effective and their work more interesting. Yet only 14 percent of first-line managers and 24 percent of middle managers would readily trust the advice of intelligent IT systems in making business decisions in the future. By contrast, nearly half of senior executives (46 percent) would readily trust the advice of intelligent systems.[14]

How can the trust gap be closed? When first-line and middle managers were asked what would allow them to trust a system's advice, 60 percent selected, "Provide a solid understanding of how the system works and generates advice," 55 percent selected "Choose a system with a proven track record," and 49 percent selected "Ensure that the system explains its logic."

By satisfying these three demands, leaders will be better positioned to capture the synergies that are possible when machines augment managers' performance. Without trust, it's unlikely an organization will be able to do more than automate a few routine managerial tasks.

Judgment Work Defined

Judgment work is about applying intellectual curiosity, experience and expertise to critical business decisions and practices when the information available is insufficient to suggest a successful course of action.

Interviews with industry leaders revealed three broad categories of judgment work:

Discernment

While intelligent machines are useful in revealing patterns and correlations, they are unable to interpret the true meaning of numbers, statistics or words. Marketing organizations have been among the first to recognize the distinction. They can use algorithms, for example, to calculate the economic impact of a marketing campaign on sales growth. But it takes human wisdom and experience to assess the relative importance of promotions that generate near-term sales and investments that build long-term brand equity.

Abstract thinking

When human beings provide rules and descriptions, intelligent machines are remarkably good at identifying classes of objects (e.g., different kinds of animals in the massive volume of photographs on the Internet). But without human guidance, computers are incapable of the "outside the box" thinking that, say, led Uber's founders to see the potential of on-demand transportation services delivered by everyday people using their own cars.

Contextual reasoning

When managers don't have all the answers or information they need to make a fully informed decision, they fill in the "gray areas" with historical, cultural and interpersonal context. Successful venture capitalists, for example, use contextual understanding to underpin their investment strategies.

Managers Must do More Strategic Judgment Work

When managers are no longer chained to routine and lower-value activities, they will have more head space to manage ideas, innovations and relationships and make better decisions that will grow the company.

Many managers, of course, already do a lot of judgment. But the truth is also that too many mundane responsibilities often prevent managers from tapping fully into their intellectual curiosity and giving more strategic judgment the attention it deserves.

Intelligent machines are poised to change this. They can, for instance, analyze the characteristics of job applicants, predict which ones will leave, and recommend strategies to get them to stay. These types of routine tasks are expected to be most impacted by intelligent machines in the future. When machines assume these coordination and control activities, some management roles will inevitably disappear while others will expand.

Figure 7.5 – The Growing Need for Judgment Work in Leadership[15]

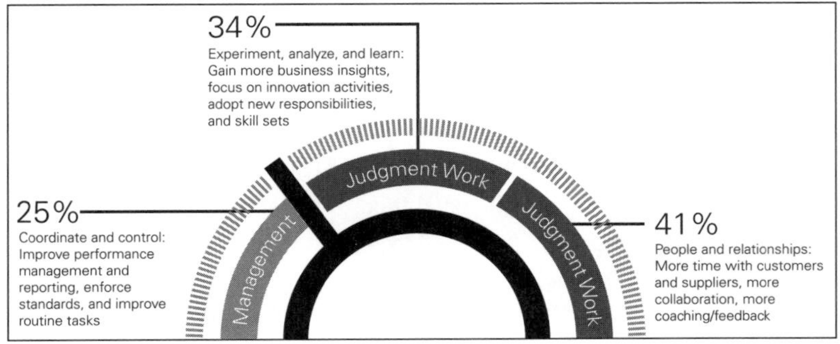

The Next-Generation Manager

Treats Intelligent Machines as Colleagues

The next-generation manager will view intelligent machines as colleagues. While judgment is a distinctly human skill, intelligent machines can accelerate human learning that supports it, assisting in data-driven simulations, scenarios, and search and discovery activities.

Focuses on Judgment Work

Some decisions require insight beyond what data can tell us. This is the sweet spot for human judgment, the application of experience and expertise to critical business decisions and practices.

Does "Real" Work – Passing off Administrative Tasks to AI

As the conventional manager role – coordinating and controlling other people's work – wanes or even vanishes, managers will turn their attention to "real" work. They will become leading practitioners, not just administrators, sharing much with managers in creative and problem solving businesses, such as art directors at design agencies, chief surgeons at hospitals, principle investigators in science, or project managers in management consulting.

Collaborates Digitally across Boundaries

The next-generation manager will need high social intelligence to collaborate effectively in teams and networks, teasing out and bringing together diverse perspectives, insights and experiences to support collective judgment, complex problem solving and ideation. He or she will also use digital technologies to tap into the knowledge and judgment of partners, customers, external stakeholders and role models in other industries.

Works Like a Designer

While a manager's creative abilities are vital, perhaps even more important is the ability to harness others' creativity. Manager-designers master the craft of bringing together diverse ideas into integrated, workable and appealing solutions. They embed design thinking in their teams' and organizations' practices. Intelligent machines will enable and accelerate design-like work processes, such as supporting problem representation, data and solution visualization, and digital and physical prototyping.

Under-Appreciated Intelligent Machines

Intelligent machines can accelerate decision-making and learning and they can make human judgment better. Analytics and artificial intelligence can, for example, help improve manager's social skills and their abilities to read the emotions of others.

In a very concrete application, intelligent machines can analyze positive and negative language during interactions with customers, employees or peers and report that feedback and advice back to managers. Thus they can improve manager relationships with peers and fellow decision-makers. These interpersonal skills will be critical to enabling a collaborative mindset around judgment.

Intelligent machines can also make it easier – and less risky and costly – for managers to test hypotheses or conduct search and discovery. R&D managers can use machines to produce data models that will help them place the right bets on new products or services, while marketing managers can use the analyses generated by intelligent machines to design data-driven customer experiences.

Unfortunately, many of today's managers are blind to the fact that intelligent machines can help them be more effective in applying judgment to drive organizational performance, growth, agility and innovation. But this is about to change naturally as IT-savy Millennials fill more and more management positions.

83 percent of them trust advice from machines, compared to 66 percent of baby boomers. They have also embraced the need to learn more creative thinking and analytical and interpretative skills, while baby boomers tend to focus on sharpening current skills.[16]

These findings suggest that as Millennials advance in their careers, their appreciation of intelligent machines will continue to push the boundaries of machine-assisted judgment work. They also suggest that Millennials can offer unique and valuable perspectives to today's more experienced executives through mechanisms such as shadow advisory boards.

Corporate HR's Need for a Strategic Stance

Based on all this, how severe is your own skills gap?

With the migration from human-centric to machine-centric manufacturing, there is a major risk that the shortage of suitable candidates for a swiftly expanding digital job market will coincide with a glut of out-of-date qualifications.

Skills and qualifications will have much shorter shelf lives. As the World Economic Forum (WEF) points out in a study on employment trends, the occupations or qualifications most in-demand due to changing industrial operating models did not even exist ten years ago. It says that job profiles change so quickly now that two out of three children starting elementary school today will one day work jobs as yet unnamed.[17]

The following list (Figure 7.6) we put together in a consultancy paper for a tier one automotive supplier shows the probabilities of various industrial jobs becoming obsolete due to their "computerizability."

Figure 7.6 – Industrial Jobs by Vulnerability to Computer Replacement Within Two Decades[18]

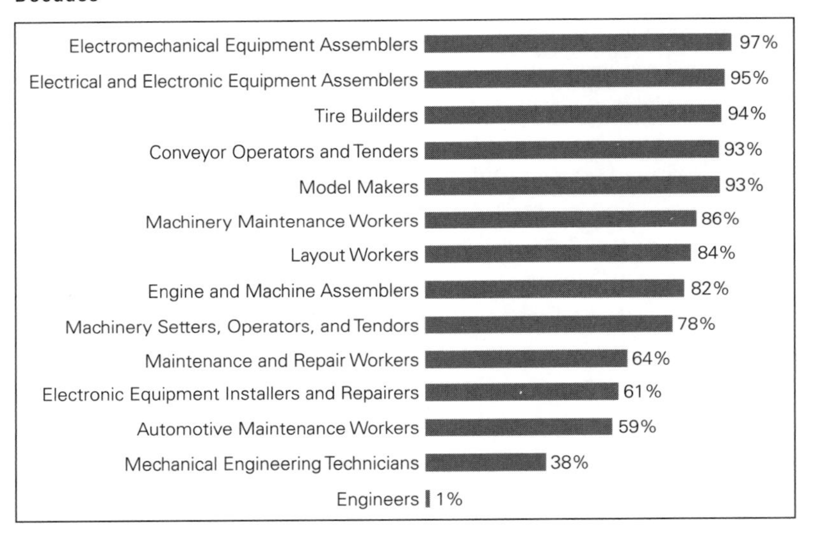

This is vital research. Enterprises must anticipate job trends and necessary skills a generation in advance. Otherwise they could easily discover they have done everything right technologically but are without staff for their upgraded businesses. Note, again, the somewhat counter-intuitive result: far from allowing employers to dispense with human employment, automation actually makes it more challenging.

Recruitment departments must adopt a much more strategic stance for spotting the right candidates and skills at the right time. Enterprises can no longer afford to bank on disconnected, anonymous labor markets delivering shift workers as needed. Instead they must adopt an active role, either developing talent within their organizations or helping educational institutions shape curricula and produce adequate numbers of degrees.

On the other hand, businesses should also prepare to tap an increasingly crowdsourced external workforce. Just like the crowd-based transport network created among private car owners by Uber, future labor market platforms will create a pool of expertise that is made transparent and accessible for momentary employers via digital technology. In the future, this model of employment will make enterprises depend on vast numbers of often highly skilled freelance temps, not traditional payroll employees.

Millennials, should be high on the recruitment list. The most populous generation alive, by 2020 there will be 86m of them working in the United States – 40 percent of the working population. They are the first crop of true digital natives, used to both sharing personal data and having instant access to information about individuals, products and companies. They will therefore filter more easily into a digitized enterprise environment. Furthermore, they have insider understanding of what younger consumers want from products and services. Such personnel will be highly valuable and, to keep them, companies will need to provide appealing work environments – something Google understood early.

But permanent upskilling and redeployment of existing workforces is viable depending on the sector. Conventional jobs in manufacturing and production are especially suited to this. Adequately executed, upskilling demonstrates once again that, more and more, intelligent manufacturing technology is not about removing jobs but creating new ones, often more stimulating than the old.

The WEF study shows that three job profiles will be especially sought after the more the digital revolution progresses.[19]

Data analysts will be much in demand – hardly surprising considering the imperative of extracting actionable data throughout manufacturing processes and functions, from supply chains to products in the field.

Connected products will be increasingly complicated to explain. The more industrial sectors approach the Outcome Economy and software-generated business results are in demand, the more customers will need advice, service and training. Specialized sales representatives will be needed, another example of how the new environment can enrich old roles. This is sales well beyond the traditional grind of persuasion, targets and commissions.

Finally, again, senior managers will be needed to handle and push forward the epic change businesses have to go through when they are digitally transformed. I have already indicated how managers will need to be much more collaborative and non-hierarchical than is generally the case today. At the same time, almost paradoxically, their responsibilities will be enormous. They will have to be able to uproot and refit complex work streams, create whole new digital work cultures and make sure changes function and reap productivity gains. It is no surprise that many business leaders see a digital change manager as one of the most important roles in their future enterprises.

Takeaways

1. The industrial worker of the future will be a data-based decision-maker and supervisory presence on the factory floor, in the engineering centers or on the field servicing products.

2. All business roles and functions will be affected as cobots and artificial intelligence will permeate the enterprise resulting in a blended workforce from the shop floor to the boardroom.

3. Don't wait – proactively manage this revolutionary change in your company.

4. Craft new training and recruitment strategies now – start-up skilling your workforce and recruiting the talent now as the right skills will be in short supply. Explore new digital workforce models such as crowdsourcing.

5. Focus on your line managers, they will be critical in seeding and steering the change of your entire workforce while undergoing significant changes themselves.

Chapter 8

Zoom in: How to Master Innovation in the New

What customers want and expect from businesses are no longer just bigger, better, faster or even smaller products and services. Businesses must be much more accurate in anticipating what customers require, even before the customers sense it themselves. That requires a new demand-driven approach to innovation, one without barriers and boundaries in enterprise organizations, that is agile and open to external input from extended ecosystems and pays close attention to digital feedback loops from the end-user market. Four types of innovators are currently identifiable in global business practice. Only one, the Brilliant Innovator, well-prepared to drive business value in the New, is qualified to be sustainably successful in the near future when the Outcome Economy becomes the norm.

For the best part of modern industrial history, innovation pushes of incumbent manufacturing sectors' innovation pushes have focused on additional functionalities or qualities for existing products. Car technology, for example, has been pushed towards ever more horsepower, fuel efficiency, and safety, while the car's digital experience was neglected.

The routine task of development engineers and designers was thinking up new features or product generations that would make physical hardware items saleable in high volume to increasingly refined market niches. Innovative progress was incremental not revolutionary.

But innovation pushes of this sort have yielded fewer and fewer "major steps" over the last century. Where the 1940s, 1950s and 1960s saw the heydays of breakthrough innovations such as semiconductors, supersonic flight or advanced radar technology, in later years the pace and number of breakthroughs steadily slowed.

This is to a certain extent even true for quantum leap innovations such as the smartphone. Its inception, disruptive as it seemed about ten years ago, had on the one hand the character of a mere technological extension. Data-enabled mobile phones had been around for years before an Internet-enabled mobile device with a large touch screen became the staple gadget of todays digitally connected world.

But this is the point: the smartphone is a real breakthrough innovation, but it is so in being a platform product, embedded in its own ecosystem of software applications and application creators. Here, software, experience and the platform that enable them are what create the value of what is actually a rather "dumb" piece of microelectronics. And this sets the direction for future breakthroughs.

The wider problem with this in the swiftly emerging digital world is that many incumbent enterprises' R&D units and activities are often stuck in a legacy rut – compartmentalized in silos and heavily focused on legacy products and services. Many of them also make hardly any effort to embed any analytics capability within a state-of-the-art platform approach. This makes most of them unprepared to challenge digital disruption.

Yes, many companies are making good progress in creating e-commerce portals or managing their customer relationships digitally. But their R&D departments remain insular, without wider integrated analytics capabilities or platforming approaches with smart links to the Internet of Things (IoT) outside their own walls.

Their set of innovation tasks is about to become much more complex. On the one hand they will need to fire up innovation in legacy activities that still earn good money and which will do so for a while. On the other, they must push innovation in the New, giving shape to connected products and services of a totally new character, compatible with the approaching outcome I have been describing. A bifurcated approach is necessary to cover these two strands.

Studies found that many companies struggle to master such bifurcation. Around a thousand of the world's largest companies spent $650bn on research and development in 2014 according to their survey – an increase of over 6 percent per year over the last five years. Enough funding is dedicated to innovation, it seems. What matters is less how much than how it is allocated.[1]

Although 63 percent of companies we surveyed have a Chief Innovation Officer, 26 percent still have no formal or no system at all in place to achieve innovation, let alone divide it strategically into two strands.[2]

Bear in mind that an innovation system, in the old as well as in the New, is a complex set-up comprising an effective idea engine, eco-system scouting, talent and governance. It is not easy to get started, never mind splitting it in two.

Old-Style Innovators See Only the Market's Supply Side

Incumbent companies, sizable as they are, need to adopt the capabilities and pioneering mindsets of small start-up incubators or they will systematically consume their own competitive edge.

The prevailing mindset among their innovator teams is still: "What can we do to get buyers to like what we already have by tweaking the offering?" This is indeed what innovators for existing products and services still in demand should continue asking themselves. Innovators in the New, however, should also ask: "What can we do to disrupt – to give clients what they don't yet know they want?"

Too much research and development activity is still locked into only the first question. Here, an "inside out" view of the world prevails instead of a more multidimensional picture comprising connected cross-industry inputs and joint cross-industry outputs – for instance in the form of new development alliances and profit-sharing partnerships. Similarly, there are often no cross-functional strategies to integrate innovators with IT and solution product managers within companies.

Old-school innovation approaches are still firmly built on a fundamental supply-side perspective. They focus on end-user markets, too often anticipating future market volumes through demographic research, assessing acceptability of a product with focus groups and estimates of potential sales figures before deciding whether to go ahead with marketing. "Build it and they will come," is a mantra still heard often.

In practice, of course, markets sometimes reject what engineers and marketers were sure would be a killer offering and propositions that tested less well at times achieve stellar market reception. The history of innovation is littered with spectacular misjudgements. Think of the famous prediction by 20th Century Fox luminary Darryl F. Zanuck: "Television won't be able to hold on to any market share it captures after the first six months. People will soon get tired of staring at a plywood box every night."[3] Or there's the prognosis that "Nuclear-powered vacuum cleaners will probably be a reality within ten years," from an American domestic appliances manufacturer in the 1950s.[4]

"Build it and They Will Come" vs. "Let Them Come and We Will Build it"

The orientation towards the market's supply side is no longer state-of-the-art. The data-driven Outcome Economy will significantly move the goal posts for new propositions.

In the future, nimble, open, demand-driven innovation will be the norm and customers will be offered new and fluid service experiences. Innovators will be in demand who can anticipate and meet these fast and frequently changing market needs in near real-time, using information gleaned from sources such as social listening. Each consumer or client will be his or her own very individual consumer group, able to indulge a taste for luxury in the morning and frugality at night or largesse in the car but thrift at home. The world will be that agile.

As I stated earlier (Chapter 2), the future will be defined by sales of outcomes. Companies will offer services and experiences around a physical software-enabled product instead of the product itself, which will primarily function as a mere container.

Power drill manufacturers – or for that matter any service provider in possession of a drill – will sell the outcome of holes in the wall, complete with a plug and hook to put up the picture, rather than just a power tool. A builder of forklift trucks will offer software for steering the whole truck fleet in warehouses to meet customer demand for maximum logistical efficiency. And carmakers will sell safe trips provided by autonomous cars and in-car services such as software that makes the car a seamless extension of the office.

To succeed in this world in which future markets crucially hinge on software and the innovation of digital experiences, companies must evolve their innovation DNA. They must keep in mind that the world will soon be dotted with millions of products smartened by digital code enabling copious data flow from products back to development engineers at innovation units. Analyzed, rehashed and refined insights will be their major raw material, feeding into their ideation processes for new products and services.

The data loopback described is decisive as it imposes a demand-driven momentum on enterprises. Product and service clients in the field will act as "permanent beta" reporters and feedbackers for corporate research and development teams. "Build it and they will come," will turn into "Let them come and we will build it."

Achieving this will require drastic changes in mindsets and innovation processes. This cuts across all operations and collaborations with customers and partners. It equally requires a new lens on competitors and the ability to operate in more open and fluid ecosystems.

Success in data-driven markets rests on leveraging data insights. But it is also based on the feedback intelligence of the crowd, the ability to master multiple development lifecycles simultaneously, the implementation of digital platform technology and partnering with outside innovators. In the end, all this is in the name of product and service solutions oriented around precise customer needs.

The First Boosts From Innovation in the New

Innovation priorities have noticeably begun to shift, and not just in digitally intensive markets such as telecommunications, consumer electronics or software. Businesses across many sectors, including industrial engineering, are slowly beginning to rewrite their innovation playbooks.

Recent global research across industries found that 42 percent of companies say improved customer experience is where they've seen the greatest success from innovation in the last two years – pointing to a growing understanding of the Outcome Economy.[5] The research also shows that leading enterprises are starting to look beyond simply differentiating legacy products and services, making preparations to create increasingly complex customer solutions with higher value and enhanced experiences. The table in Figure 8.1 indicates who is at the forefront with what approach.

The businesses studied are seeing promising results from their innovations. Business leaders, depending on how much emphasis they put on new ways to innovate, report between 3.5 and 7 percent higher revenues and profitability, directly attributable to new and better innovation approaches.

The extent of those higher revenues is shown in Figure 8.2, with industrial equipment, consumer goods and consumer electronics sectors profiting most from new ways to innovate.

Figure 8.1 – Re-Engineering Innovation to Change the Overall Customer Experience[6]

Company	Description
Monsanto	Monsanto is offering targeted intelligence to farmers in real-time, helping them maximize yields in any weather and soil condition. The offering also feeds back to Monsanto by using the weather and yield data to develop better farming products so they can offer a more personalized experience to farmers.
Disney	Disney created the "Magic Band" to provide customers with an optimized and seamless experience throughout their time at Disney World, while providing a valuable source of customer insights.
John Deere	John Deere transformed its business by moving beyond pure equipment to providing farmers with digital services such as crop advisories, weather alerts, planting prescriptions and seeding population advice.
Dow Chemical	Dow operationalized collaborations with customers/partners in its value chain through its "Pack Center" facilities: cutting-edge testing labs and technical teams that more closely align it with customer needs and wants.
Lego	Lego, far from being just a manufacturer of plastic components, is today, at its core, a design firm, engaged in conceiving experiences that extend physical play into virtual and digital worlds. To bolster its design capabilities, the company now collaborates with retailers, academics, and technology inventors.
BMW	Auto giant BMW generates deep end-customer insights through its customer-oriented sales and production process (COSP), an online ordering system that enables customers to personalize their vehicle orders up to eight working days before assembly begins, with no impact on delivery deadlines. COSP records and processes nearly 120,000 modification requests a month and feeds directly into the manufacturing planning department. The system not only enables near real-time adjustments to production schedules but also gives BMW more immediate and accurate insights into how customers' preferences, needs, and tastes are shifting.
Xiaomi	Crowdsourcing development of mobile phone features allows China's Xiaomi to bypass traditional R&D spend.
Honda	Honda invested in rapid prototyping to accelerate product introduction and seek feedback on design(s).

Four Innovator Types, One Long-Term Winner

Studies also analyzed the practices and value performances of 350 businesses from eight industries: automotive, industrial equipment, consumer goods, medical devices, enterprise technology, consumer technology, communications technology and software. To get a global spread, we further looked into nine countries – the US, Canada, the UK, France, Germany, Italy, China, Japan, and South Korea – where we interviewed chief technology officers, division presidents and division vice presidents of engineering and innovation, or holders of equivalent roles.

Figure 8.2 – Impact of New Innovation Approaches[7]

	Revenue % Increase	Revenue Increase in Millions
Life Sciences/Medical Products/Biotech	5.0%	$581
Consumer Technology	5.3%	$633
Industrial Equipment	7.0%	$567
Enterprise Technology	3.9%	$355
Automotive	4.8%	$1,009
Communications Equipment Technology	3.5%	$301
Consumer Goods & Services	5.5%	$395
Software	4.0%	$450

	Operating Income CAGR % Averages (2011-2014)	Impact on Operating Income CAGR % Due to Improvement in Value Creation Performance
Life Sciences/Medical Products/ Biotech	1.2%	3.7%
Consumer Technology	24.9%	27.5%
Industrial Equipment	2.0%	5.5%
Enterprise Technology	13.6%	15.5%
Automotive	7.7%	10.0%
Communications Equipment Technology	17.0%	18.7%
Consumer Goods & Services	6.6%	9.3%
Software	5.3%	7.3%

Filtering down our findings, we were able to extract four innovator types, each with a characteristic approach to tackling the New (see Figure 8.3).

The first, and most common at 43 percent, we called the **Market Share Protector**. This describes a business basically following the old innovation rulebook, spending on research and development fairly moderately, just enough to come up with enough product and service innovations to defend a *status quo* market share. The bulk of innovation is conducted in the legacy strands of products and services.

Figure 8.3 – Innovation-Driven Growth Model[8]

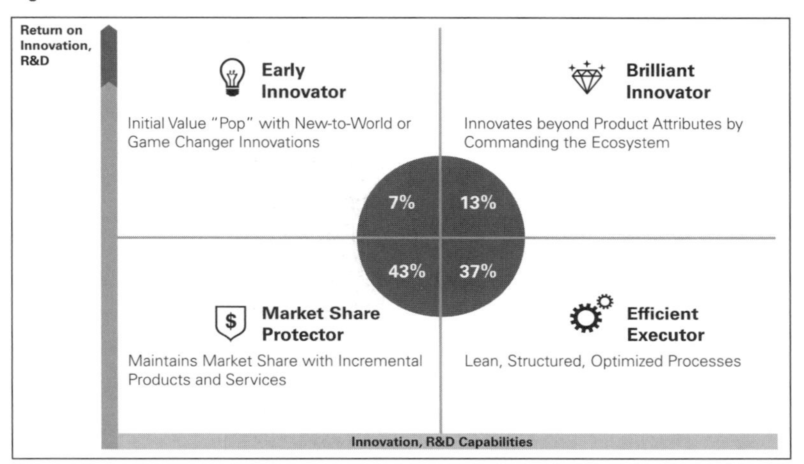

The second type we dubbed the **Efficient Executor**. This is an enterprise with significantly more innovation efficiency thanks to a much more stringent policy towards streamlining innovation processes. But, surprisingly, this does not translate into higher innovation returns, as this type has not yet arrived at new-style innovation setups involving all the ingredients we have been discussing – from connected products and platform designs to alliances with outside ecosystem partners.

Increased returns were realized by the third type, the **Early Innovator**. This is a business with agile and responsive start-up-style innovation processes, leading to breakthrough innovations resulting from a "light-bulb moment." Such innovations are sufficient to change whole markets or carve out completely new market segments and the businesses are duly able to keep their pioneer returns going for a good while. Thus, their return and efficiency are significantly higher than the first two innovator types.

Brilliant Innovators Lead the Way in the Industrial Sector

In the same higher-return bracket is a fourth innovator type, which we see as the role model for modern industrial manufacturers in the Outcome Economy.

This is the **Brilliant Innovator.** It combines the Efficient Executor's systematic innovation efficiency with the Early Innovator's innovative power and resulting return levels. The social media platform Facebook is a good example, having made the journey from Early Innovator to Brilliant Innovator, with a real talent for creating solutions around customer experiences.

Industrial business are now also aspiring to become Brilliant Innovators. German engineering firm Bosch has, for instance, launched its own IoT cloud for web-based services. In it Bosch runs applications for its connected mobility, connected industries and connected buildings businesses – with the stated aim of entering completely new fields and customers. Thus the IoT cloud provides a huge variety of connected services that range from enabling consumers to reserve parking spots prior to arriving at their destinations, to remote troubleshooting for heating engineers, and to providing farmers with exact understanding of ground temperatures in order to improve harvest and yield.[9]

Health technology specialist Carestream is similary expanding its digital value proposition well beyond centralized clinical imaging departments, making its imaging and informatics solutions available to areas such as orthopedics, intensive care, emergency department, intraoperative and bedside imaging. And the company uses its technologies to create wider healthcare collaboration and information-sharing capabilities.[10]

Microchip maker Intel is also spurring the development of new products that use its chips to expand the market for semiconductors. Thus it has entered the drones business through a series of acquisitions and continues to invest in drone technologies. Intel acquired Ascending Technologies in 2016 following its $60m purchase of Shanghai-based drone and aerospace company Yuneec International. It has also made investments in other drone companies, namely Airware and Precision Hawk.[11]

All these businesses recognize the need to move to the upper right quadrant in our innovator chart because new digital business lines are an imperative for survival in the future.

I recommend that all manufacturing companies aim to become Brilliant Innovators. Early Innovators obviously do well, but there is probably no way to engineer this position with certainty, given that it is based on lightbulb inspiration moments. It is also impractical for existing large manufacturers with still successful legacy products. Finally, as Facebook shows, for really sustainable success, even Early Innovators should probably aim to become Brilliant Innovators too.

The Brilliant Innovator pole position can only be achieved when the full-spectrum new innovation culture I have outlined is implemented throughout the organization: no silos, free data flow, effective feedback loops, connected products, and real-time reaction to market shifts and customer attitudes.

As Figure 8.3 shows, we found that 43 percent of businesses are Market Share Protectors and 37 percent are Efficient Executors. So a full 80 percent of businesses across all sectors are still running innovation units that do not use the playbook for innovation in the New. In that, they are mere Renovators.

Brilliant Innovators represent only 13 percent of companies we studied and the Early Innovators are even rarer at only 7 percent,

Figure 8.4 – Specific Actions to Make the Move from One Quadrant to Another[12]

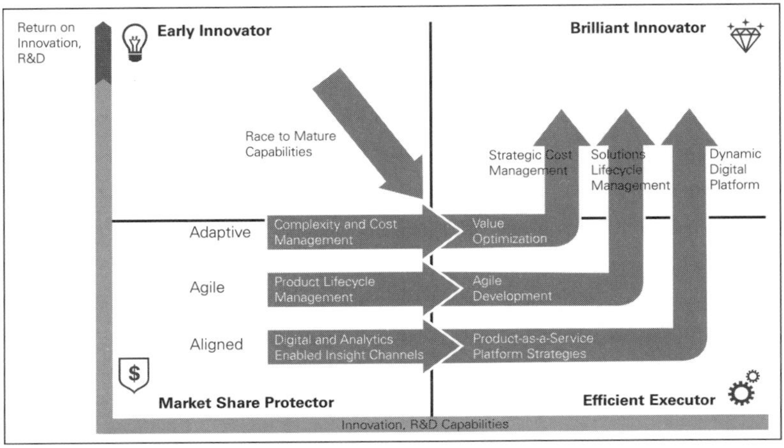

Return on Innovation, R&D
Early Innovator
Brilliant Innovator
Race to Mature Capabilities
Strategic Cost Management
Solutions Lifecycle Management
Dynamic Digital Platform
Adaptive
Complexity and Cost Management
Value Optimization
Agile
Product Lifecycle Management
Agile Development
Aligned
Digital and Analytics Enabled Insight Channels
Product-as-a-Service Platform Strategies
Market Share Protector
Efficient Executor
Innovation, R&D Capabilities

which, again, can probably be explained by the fact that game-changing innovations *per se* are rare and often the outcome not of systematic R&D activity but ad hoc ingenuity. (As an aside, very few industrial manufacturers on the list score really high in this type of innovation, but one that does is 3M.) The select few Early Innovators and Brilliant Innovators are high performers, true Reinventors, enjoying greater return on investment and market share than their peers.

Perhaps surprisingly, our findings also show that these higher returns do not necessarily come from greater financial investment in innovation. The results rather illustrate that all innovator types have more or less the same innovation investment profiles. What makes the difference is the Reinventors' better knowledge of efficient innovation approaches and how to leverage them. This is why true Reinventors simply generate significantly higher results from the same investment: 3.5-7 percent annualized revenue lift and a corresponding growth in operating income compared to their industry peers.

Figure 8.5 – Innovation Investment Allocation[13]

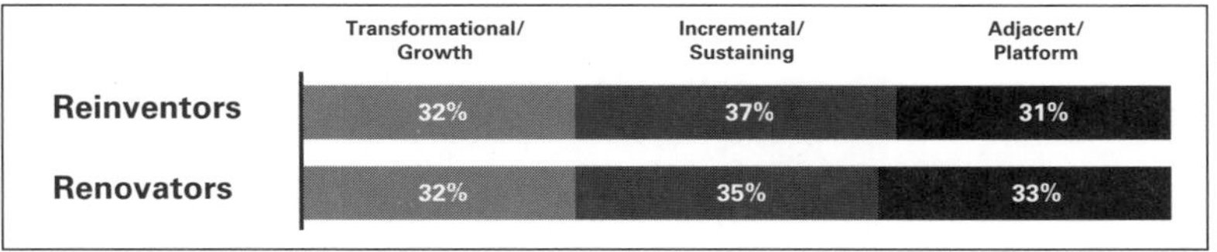

Digitally-Driven Innovation Makes all the Difference

We asked our sample businesses to rank the procedures, methods and approaches they use in their innovation activity. Unsurprisingly, the list for Reinventors looks significantly different from the one for Renovators (see Figure 8.6).

Figure 8.6 – Customer/Consumer Insight Methods[14]

Reinventors Top 5	Renovators Top 5
1. Insights from Crowdsourcing or External User Data	1. Trend Monitoring and Forecasting
2. Online Research Tool	2. Tailoring to Global Markets
3. Ethnographic Research	3. Big Data Mining
4. Social Media Listening and Integration	4. Channel Insights (Distributors, Retailers)
5. Channel Insights (Distributors, Retailers)	5. Competitor Insights

"Using Insights from crowdsourcing or external user data," for instance, ranked number one in the Reinventor list, indicating permeable structures, agile processes, flexible docking options for external innovation partners and quickly built ecosystem links. The use of online research tools and social media listening are also crucial when it comes to exploiting the full advantages of creating digital consumer experience.

One can see that Renovators are hardly digital luddites since they use big data mining and channel insights. However, their number one tool, trend monitoring and forecasting, strongly points at traditional supply-side market views and a largely conventional innovation set-up. Essentially, they take a well-trodden innovation path centered around more and improved product features.

Reinventors accelerate faster to outsized returns from their innovation and R&D capabilities. Brilliant Innovators are especially gifted at finding new ways to connect with customers through cutting-edge innovation processes, platforms and ecosystems in which the product or service is just one dimension of a much larger value proposition.

You can see in Figure 8.7 that it works. Our research found Reinventors significantly superior in all criteria for financial success in an Outcome Economy: time to market, rate of product introduction, creating digital customer experiences, spotting relevant trends.

Figure 8.7 – Innovation Capabilities Leveraged[15]

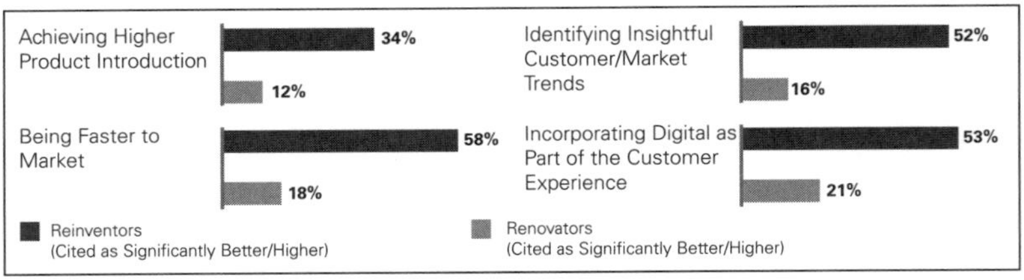

Achieving Higher Product Introduction 34% 12%

Being Faster to Market 58% 18%

Identifying Insightful Customer/Market Trends 52% 16%

Incorporating Digital as Part of the Customer Experience 53% 21%

Reinventors (Cited as Significantly Better/Higher)

Renovators (Cited as Significantly Better/Higher)

Four Recommendations for Becoming a Reinventor

Making the move from one quadrant to another, with the aim of ending up a Reinventor, companies must implement innovation models resting on four main pillars:

1. Build an insight platform. This creates new revenue through continuously renewing combinations of products, services and experiences that dynamically change and adapt.

Knowing your customers and consumers has always been vital, but in this multi-dimensional landscape of balanced products, services and experiences, you can no longer just ask customers what they want, you must meet their as yet unmet and possible even yet appreciated needs. This becomes more important the more customers are redefined not as a monolithic group but as individuals of one. See again in the following table (Figure 8.8) who is already leading here.

Such understanding is the lifeblood of the Brilliant Innovators. Accordingly, our study shows that 63 percent of leaders are today making improvements to their advanced analytics and other methods listed in Figure 8.6 to better understand the customer and 31 percent have plans to do the same in the short term.

2. Be solution-centric. The new competitive world is multi-dimensional. While businesses clearly must continue improving and augmenting existing products and services, they must also focus broadly and deeply on the ecosystem of experiences and connections they support and provide. Services, experiences, hardware and software should all be connected and centered around the customer.

That requires a major realignment. Business silos must cease to exist; R&D, engineering, manufacturing, supply chain, sales and marketing are all equally accountable for innovation and must pursue it collaboratively and in alignment. Existing walls between different product lines must be torn down so offerings can start to complement each other and give customers bigger value and better experience. A shift in mindset is required where implications for innovation-driven growth are no longer linear but continuous, dynamic and agile.

Figure 8.8 – Analytics-Driven Insights Create Higher Value Customer Experiences[16]

Company	Description
Verizon	Verizon is aiming to drive new revenue using subscriber data, based on omni-channel consumer mobile marketing behavior from connected devices across a nationwide mobile network.
Caterpillar	Caterpillar formed a partnership with Uptake to provide predictive analytics on equipment health based on onboard telematics data. This resulted in increased asset productivity for customers.
Rolls-Royce	Rolls-Royce uses sensors and predictive analytics to monitor its jet engines and make recommendations to its customers on maintenance to increase uptime and reduce total cost of ownership.
Netflix	Netflix used insights from customer viewing habits to predict the potential market size for its House of Cards show and that Kevin Spacey and David Fincher would likely be a successful star and director.
Pitney Bowes	Pitney Bowes' Single Customer View software solution helps organizations enhance and deepen their understanding of customers in the digital era. Single Customer View allows to rapidly design, deliver, and evolve contextually-relevant views about a customer in real-time across all channels.
Alibaba - Taobao	Alibaba's trading platform, Taobao, is an example of a product that emerged from deep insights into how customers were underserved, addressing their inability to connect with suppliers and offering sophisticated understanding of the Chinese banking system. Taobao wouldn't have happened without Alibaba's deep, analytically driven understanding of customers.
Cedar Sinai	Cedar Sinai has enabled HealthKit integration in its hospital to aggregate data from over 80,000 patients using over 900 Healthkit-enabled apps and devices. Cedar Sinai's initiative will help doctors deliver better healthcare with increased visibility into their patients' health data. In addition, it will reduce treatment time for patients with better localization of their healthcare data.
CPG companies	CPG companies are now incorporating real-time retailer sales data into their forecasts, allowing them increased agility in response to market changes while better optimizing inventories (demand sensing, but not demand insight).

3. Drive pivotal leadership. This is leadership that orchestrates, activates and influences enterprise-wide change. It requires leaders at the helm capable of seeing value where others can't, setting the right course and charting progress. Good technology companies employ solution managers as pivotal leaders, where other sectors use relatively traditional product or brand managers more focused on incremental sales than breakthrough solutions.

Our survey points to two clear characteristics that Reinventors get right. They set the adequate vision and they establish the metrics by which success can be assessed and monitored. What's more, our survey also confirms that they prioritize key areas above others, putting emphasis on, strategy-driven product management, leadership vision and program execution.

4. Operate at multiple speeds. Benchmarks of success in the new innovation playbooks cannot be the same performance indicators as used in the past and time to market, in particular, is no longer a source of long-term differentiation because everybody will be reacting incredibly fast to market cues. Reinventors understand the need to operate at multiple speeds simultaneously, reflecting the different requirements of digital and traditional product and service innovation cycles.

The results finally show that Reinventors continue to permanently develop distinctive and dynamic innovation approaches and capabilities. In other words, they're constantly rewriting their innovation playbook. It is a process well reflected in the following table.

Incubator Mentalities and Capabilities Round off Future Innovation

As we have seen, large companies, feeling the heat, are starting to inch closer to new and speedier innovation mindsets. Where typical innovation cycles in pre-digital and product-centric times ranged up to seven years, now it is often down to only two or three years and in many cases only months.

Still, to shift from traditional, static and anticipatory innovation models to agile incubator capabilities, gaining the responsive innovation brain and muscle of a start-up, is a challenge, particularly given the need for a bifurcated approach between legacy offerings and the New.

Incubator services, offered by a company-owned team of innovation experts looking into all processes across all functions, strength-

Figure 8.9 – Concurrent Innovation Model[17]

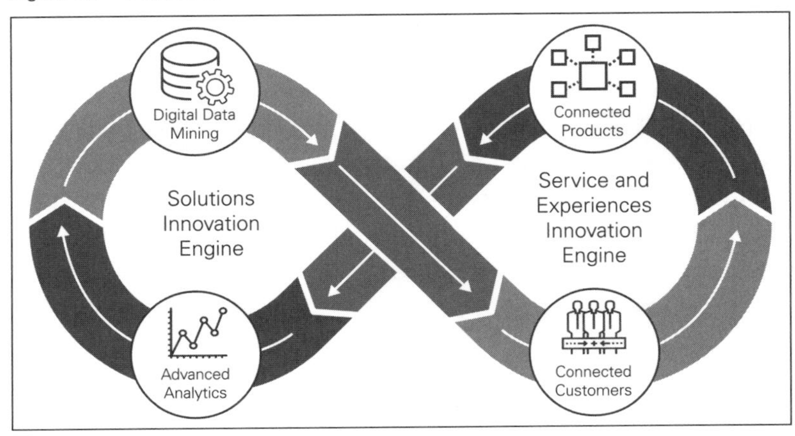

en a company's ability to identify disruptive moves that lead to growth.

A Leading Tier 1 Automotive Supplier Runs an Internal Incubator to Speed up New Ideas

A leading tier 1 automotive supplier set up an Incubator Program Office (IPO) in 2014 to foster and launch projects and business ideas that are linked to mobility and its wider core business.

The IPO has been created as a designated, start-up-style internal unit, spanning all continents. It hunts for new business ideas within its own parent but also outside it. Internally, it consults staff of all ranks and functions for potential future ideas, while externally it collaborates with innovators situated in its wider ecosystem outside its own organization.

If a suggestion qualifies, the IPO pushes its further development as far as possible to test market levels. Within five years, the incubator aims at extracting a viable portfolio of new companies or projects from its regional hubs in Europe, China and the US. And acting in the mode of a start-up, the IPO also aborts around 30 percent of its projects when they are identified as lacking promise.

Among the priority domains to explore are new tire material composites for high deflection structures, business applications that leverage the company's expertise in tire design, or novel products and services that will enhance the mobility of goods and persons by leveraging IT.

Analysis of the market landscape and understanding the associated dynamics, innovation patterns were critical when setting up and operating the IPO. Various possible futures were also envisioned through a "divergence" exercise to identify, qualify and prioritize innovation spots.

Asking its employees for suggestions, the company received 4,200 contributions from Europe alone. The company also connected to the ecosystem of start-ups and acqired an ownership stake in young firms that were capable of providing solutions for certain ideas.

The IPO's practices and those of other corporate examples can be distilled into three general recommendations for becoming a Reinventor.

1. Align your business strategy and your incubator strategy. The degree of freedom is significantly wider for an incubator than traditional R&D or innovation functions, but it is essential to define innovation priorities. Incubation needs to be focused to avoid being pulled in too many directions. Is the aim a new product, connected solution, or a mobility or digital service? Companies need to choose a few and then pair the incubator to these strategically important projects.

2. Position your incubator at the proper level within the organization. The service needs to directly report to a company's innovation board structure. This type of visibility along with the right weight will ensure efforts can make headway. Guaranteeing the right level of engagement infuses confidence in the incubator as an agent for innovation. It can even unite the company, energizing all functions about the idea of generating new opportunities.

3. Develop the ecosystem with the right partners. With the necessary internal processes and approaches in place, companies will have a base from which to effectively collaborate with universities, other start-ups and third parties that complement them and supplement capability gaps. Automotive companies, for instance, need to acquire competence in telecoms, software and analytics to tackle the future challenge of the connected car. It's something Renault did when it teamed up with Paris Incubateurs. By opening itself to collaboration, Renault has gained access to a host of start-up that will help them design innovative services, applications and technologies.[18]

Schneider Electric Shows How to Best Leverage Start-up Partnerships[19]

To achieve innovation, Schneider Electric, the leading global industrial equipment manufacturer, has in its core business always closely worked with technology partners to complement their solutions and architecture both in terms of hardware and software. However, the company realized that with the emergence of the digital era and more and more of their products getting connected, it had to open up to new and very different partner businesses. These partners are different in culture, agility or maturity and many of them are start-up businesses with only limited visibility on their long-term success or market uptake. The management at Schneider Electric realized that it was up to them rather than their partners to adapt.

So how did they go about it? They set up dedicated teams across the world in charge of developing relationships with these start-ups. What is key when working with young founding firms are the "use cases". They need to be very focused and specific regarding what client issues they want to solve. Less is more when outlining your ideas.

In the old days this could not happen. Schneider Electric would set up broad based partnership at company levels, than create company-wide awareness. It was then left to the individual business units to decide whether or not to leverage the partnership. The drawback: this set-up took time. Energetic partnerships would swiftly wilt within the system leading to limited business outcomes.

Now in the new approach both partners, Schneider Electric and the start-up, focus on one or two use cases allowing for quick testing of start-up technologies in very pragmatic and quick sprints of three to six months maximum.

It is very much about change management and demonstrating the value brought to the organization but more importantly to the customer. Especially in the engineering community the mantra still too often goes: "We have the best technology, the knowledge and know what is best for the company." One of the key change levers is to have the right leaders who share a vision of the New, and of "how to make it happen" and usually they come from the outside.

The market is at a very early stage for Schneider Electric´s new software-enabled products and the opportunity (and challenge) reside in the "making the market". Anticipating the (potential) demand, allows Schneider Electric to better understand client readiness to adopt their new connected products, as well as fine-tuning the use cases – their relevance, potential business cases, pre-requisites. It is very much about understanding the why-behind-the buy of your customer, or the customer of your customer, through digital technology.

Gaining such an insight requires new approaches and methods such as ethnographic research, Design Thinking (see Chapter 4), working with channel partners, exploiting social media and understanding how the products and services will be used. This allows the company to fine-tune and align their solutions to the exact clients' expectations and focus on the minimal viable solution, which will deliver the value expected by customers. This is a very efficient way to go about innovation.

So, why are so many companies failing when it comes to rebuilding their innovation processes? Although businesses have varying awareness levels of what they can do to develop incubator capabilities, many traditional operations are failing in this new world.

Take hospitality as a striking example of how companies can be caught unaware: seismic shifts from start-ups like Airbnb rattled the foundation of the industry's operating model. Incumbents were also slow to catch on to online travel aggregators and distributors. One root cause: they underestimated the magnitude of change in the market place and the massive change that must take hold through their entire organization to compete.

Incubator services are not just about launching a new activity, a new process, or a new department within the company. They entail bringing new discipline, a new DNA, and a new mindset and infusing them throughout the company.

Takeaways

1. Experience beats product. Improved customer experience is where companies in the industrial sector have seen the greatest success from innovation in recent years.

2. New approaches to innovation can drive significant financial returns especially in sectors such as industrial equipment, consumer goods and consumer electronics.
3. Most industrial companies have very similar innovation investment profiles. The difference comes from the "how" rather than the "what."
4. Open up to the outside. A new view of competitors and the ability to work in more open and fluid ecosystems are key.
5. Brilliant Innovators are solution-centered, powered by insights, drive pivotal leadership and operate at multiple speeds.

09

Chapter 9

Zoom in: How to Make the Most of Platforms and Ecosystems

In a data-driven industrial world, being part of an ecosystem is vital for every industrial business. A second step can add even more value: the creation of a platform around a product. The latter is not necessary for all industrial firms, but the combination of both steps turn a business into an engine for innovation and growth. Business platforms and ecosystems in the Industrial Internet of Things (IIot) are complex. Building them requires business leaders to think laterally and factor in wide horizons of allies and novel business opportunities – all in the name of creating outcome-oriented product and service layouts. Such work is a drastic departure from old-style product-focused industrial strategies.

Industrial enterprises realize that their corporate value, innovation power and standing with customers will eventually depend not only on their own self-contained efforts, as has been the case for decades, but on the communal ambitions of the business ecosystems they will need to belong to.

Only such partner ecosystems will sufficiently fuel breakthrough innovation and disruptive growth opportunities. Only operating models built around such multilateral and multidimensional partnerships and open collaborative networks will create sufficient value to secure survival.

For industrial businesses, ecosystems are unavoidable. They should first and foremost aim to create these as parts of viable networks of partners with the shared aim of developing new products and services targeted at outcome-focused customers.

In a second step they can then – but need not necessarily – adopt a strategy where their products are more and more shaped as platform items so that they can serve as the nucleus further down the line for a highly value-creating product-centric ecosystem.

What is an Ecosystem and Why Build One?

Ecosystems are often open networks of strategic business partners with the common aim of driving growth and fostering innovation. From that perspective, an ecosystem is a company's competitiveness network. It forms an increasingly global, foresight-driven, multi-industry cocoon around its participating partners, consisting of cooperators, suppliers, institutions, customers and other stakeholders.

All these players connect and collaborate in order to innovate more quickly, to amalgamate complementary capabilities for better results and to react with greater agility to fast-moving consumer and business markets that increasingly demand complex outcomes rather than mono-dimensional products.

Typically ecosystems are built around intellectual property stemming from one core partner, which is combined with service hardware and various APIs and offered on an as-a-service basis to a horizontal or vertical market. The ecosystem is going to be a form of life "tissue" around you, without which you will not have the muscle to stay in business.

Most existing industrial businesses come from a decades-old world of bordered views and thinking, a world in which for instance intellectual property and data is jealously kept within ones own walls and departure from prescribed industry lines is perceived as dangerous, dubious and potentially value-destroying.

The emergence of digital technology has made these old walled gardens redundant. Technology all of a sudden allows markets to be tapped in no time by often unexpected attackers, whether start-up or rival incumbents.

Computer maker Apple would not have been able to tap the traditional banking sector´s payment market without digital technology. And carmaker BMW would not have been able to enter the mobility market by offering a rental fleet car system had there not been app technology allowing for this business model to be established without great budgetary risk. Mobile phone network operators themselves aim at replacing financial specialists such as Visa or Amex as well as mainstream banks, now that the smartphone is now also a payment device.

Ubiquitous digital technology basically means, that, in theory, a company in any sector could disrupt any other sector's market in no time and on a small budget. In that regard, technology has blurred the demarcation lines and dramatically lowered the entry and exit barriers to digitally contestable markets.

For example, Airbnb, a company founded in 2008, has become now the world's largest hotelier as of November 2013, forcing the established players in the hospitality industry to rethink their business models. In Asia, Didi and Ola are changing the way people use taxis, which is having a profound impact on the regulated taxi service industry. And, in only four years, Xiaomi has risen to become the world's third largest distributor of smartphones, putting many traditional mobile device manufacturers on notice.[1]

For the industrial sector that means that its markets are no longer under its rigid control, that in the future it will be barely sufficient to be a hardware provider of expertise filling specific market niches with engineering excellence.

More will be needed: services, built around hardware, that deliver outcome. From an operational point of view, that implies the need for the most suitable partners to design and market those services.

Industrial businesses will eventually have no choice. Tomorrow's complex hardware and software sponsored outcomes are not going to be made by the technologies a large company develops alone. Business executives must reach out to partners across the customer value chain regardless of their status as rivals or third-party vendors. They must be open to those connections as unexpected sources of innovation and they must reinvigorate their company culture and make every employee responsible for collaboration and innovation.

Only embedding in such partner networks and wider ecosystems can provide sufficient innovation speed and funds to renovate your core business, which will then provide you with the springboard for the expansion into future new business lines.

Furthermore, ecosystems can be complex in their make-up and typically evolve substantially over time. Hence, as remarked previously in this book, the ability to think through scenarios, develop and implement participation models and manage a company safely and profitably in multiple ecosystems is key and needs significant development in most companies.

Leveraging Start-ups

Good Ideas Put to Best Use – Fast

Innovation is key for start-ups, but so is go-to-market activity. The successes not only have a great concept, they are built to market and sell it to their target markets. What matters is not just the idea, but the idea, plus market fit, plus demonstrated value for the end client/customer. Start-ups that fail on any of these fronts mostly die.

Start-ups can be great enablers and accelerators in achieving your outcomes. These passionate, talented entrepreneurs have a tight focus on their market and value proposition. Fueled by risk arbitraged by venture capitalists – that is, risk based on other people's money – they need to execute quickly and create value to survive. They are unencumbered by the bureaucracy of larger organizations and have a store of capital for innovation and go-to-market larger than that of a corporate mid-level manager for the same goal. It's easy, then, to see the benefits of the right partnership with the right start-up.

There's a Start-up for That

There are hundreds of thousands of start-ups globally, with hundreds of billions of dollars in funding. We can exclude the B2C start-up and pre-series-A funded start-ups, but that still leaves a very large number focused on IoT, AI, Blockchain, robotics and automation, as well as many other horizontal industrial Internet technology domains. Add to the list, the verticalized start-ups across health care, oil and gas, transportation, government, and many other industries, and we see the tremendous abundance in innovation's supply side.

It is actually difficult to imagine any problem not already being addressed by a start-up somewhere today, although part of the fascination of the digital world is how innovation and technology can even tackle problems that may be latent or poorly appreciated at present. Data analytics now often shows us that we really didn't know what we didn't know.

So, very often, the solution you seek exists and a partnership with the relevant start-up or start-ups can enable your product and business teams to focus on the total solution as well as your brand.

With an empowered and well-resourced executive sponsor who embraces the concept of Open Innovation and is focused on outcomes, rather than innovation for innovation's sake, work with such start-ups can be hugely fruitful. The challenge is identifying problems that matter to your business so you can choose your start-up partners accordingly.

Traditional models of costly, long-cycle, in-house R&D can no longer keep up with the threat posed by thousands of innovative start-ups. But with Open Innovation stemming from surrounding ecosystems, including start-ups, enterprises can reclaim the role of digital disruptors. By working with emerging companies, they acquire the scale and resources to achieve business transformation objectives beyond the scope of the smaller players.[2]

How a Global Car Manufacturer has Created an Ecosystem

Passenger cars already point strongly to the future of connected products. Consider the case of a leading global car manufacturer selling millions cars per year.

In 2013, to stay relevant in the fast-evolving connected vehicle market and give their customers smart products fitting their needs, the company decided to launch a platform in Europe for new digital services, infotainment, navigation and maintenance for drivers. The aim, apart from offering convenient customer-oriented services, was also to improve product quality.

Today this platform connects more than half a billion cars in 20 European countries with various digital services and provides the manufacturer with valuable data insights. It is a standard feature with every new car built under the company´s core brands and customers can use the service free for the first few years.

To pull this off as an as-a-service platform, an ecosystem of various partners had to be forged. The company worked with a leading mobile phone operator for connectivity as well as map and navigation specialists as content partners.

Behind the wheel, customers operate their services via either a seven-inch touchscreen, steering wheel buttons or voice commands.

This platform is a customer-focused marketing feature. But its data insights also offer advantages for the company's business model, allowing warranty costs to be lowered and new revenue lines to be created. Thus the platform will eventually form the basis of a fully developed predictive maintenance solution. It also has the potential to turn the car manufacturer into a trader of valuable data on car and driver behavior.

The company will be trying new ideas for extending the digital value chain to ecosystem players from other industries such as insurance, payment providers, and oil, helping the company shift from a car-centric, hardware-driven business model to a platform-centric, data-driven business model.

Building an Ecosystem – How to Do it

The biggest advantage drawn from an ecosystem is its innovative power. To conduct innovation in step with highly specialized partners such as start-ups is much more effective compared to siloed in-house research and development activities.

Here is a useful list of steps (Figure 9.1) to make when it comes to creating highly effective ecosystems and using them as innovation platforms.

Just as businesses have always had to build historically deep vertical silos, from strategy down to processes in order to capture global growth opportunities, they now need to prepare for very active external collaboration, often at very localized levels.

From a managerial standpoint, this will be complex, as industrial businesses will have to create agile global organizations with a pragmatic sense for bonding that are much more permeable, flexible and inherently collaborative. That will require changes throughout the organization – in people, technology and strategy.

Business leaders must therefore set the tone and stage by declaring a shift away from products and services alone towards how the company can help customers achieve better outcomes. To lay the

Figure 9.1 – Steps for Creating an Effective Ecosystem[3]

Lessons Learned	
Set the Direction	• Clear definition of a 4-5 year future state is critical to the success of the overall ecosystem incubation
Executive Sponsorship	• Strong, committed executive sponsorship of the governance structure • Process that allows for quick decision-making and issue resolution
A Hands-on Steering Committee	• The governance structure should help with the execution of the Ecosystem Strategic Partnership strategy, e.g. identifying and facilitating other ecosystem participants
Diversify KPIs	• Define metrics and KPIs that measure the success of the Ecosystem Strategic Partnership over time; do not rely on sales numbers only
Channels, Channels, Channels	• Activate the channels from the very top; have a holistic approach to a client problem, industry channels, and operational group
Solution Roadmap	• Do not build a large portfolio of solutions; validate hypotheses with clients, industry SMEs, etc. before development; refine before investing in full-on development to increase solution ROI • Consider customer proof of concepts a solution as part of the contract
Manage Global Scope	• Don't spread resources too thin too early • Prioritize and manage geographic scope with global support teams
Early Wins/Intercept Inflight Opportunities	• Secure early wins to build and hold momentum and "mindshare" within each organization
Flexible Operating Model	• Define a flexible operating model to remain responsive to market • Ongoing joint innovation performance tracking and program management process
Change Management/ Cultural Alignment	• "One team" philosophy (process, metrics, attitude) • Treat the Ecosystem Strategic Partnership like a newly created business unit • A vision that allows the Ecosystem Strategic Partnership to focus on high-value activities that will drive results

foundations, they must recognize that employees at all levels have connections that could serve the company's ecosystem strategy.

And they must integrate collaborative technology that can help employees connect with each other, with outside organizations and with customers.

The good news is, surveys show that 78 percent of executives asked plan to pursue growth in new areas by using flexible organizational forms of collaboration such as strategic alliances, joint ventures or takeovers.

And businesses should also bear in mind the following: two thirds of companies that out-performed peers over the last three years say they encourage employees to be proactive in building relations with external stakeholders, compared with just over one third of under-performers.

How Open Innovation Weds Incumbents with Start-ups

Open Innovation is widely understood as a way for businesses to innovate, advance and often also market their technology, based on a mix of external and internal ideas and partners.

Accenture uses a methodology called Accelerated Innovation within the company's "Open-Innovation-as-a-service" capability. The aim is to increase the effectiveness of incumbent industrial businesses while engaging with the ecosystem of external start-up partners to drive business outcomes.

The process has three phases:

1. Define the Possible. In this phase, a business objective is stated and, through a design thinking approach, various related problems and opportunities are identified.

Once filtered, the shortlist of problems goes through a Minimum Viable Product (MVP) business canvas exercise, identifying what would satisfy early adopters and further articulating the opportunity for innovation and what success looks like.

At this point a start-up scan is done to look at potential partners that can address the MVP and proof of concept proposals are written.

2. Prove It Matters. This is the rapid prototyping phase where proof of concept proposals are funded and the innovation teams can start to engage with start-up user experience (UX) experts, and marketing leads to rapidly implement working prototypes.

Their function is to demonstrate feasibility as well as a business analysis of how this solution would need to roll out into the real world, with Key Performance Indicators (KPIs) attached to assess whether the desired outcomes were reached.

The aim is to see whether solutions – comprising start-up technology and additional solution elements – address the goals laid out in the prior step. This is a key validation point for the technology's effectiveness regarding the intended business outcome.

3. Make It Real. The final step in the process is to deploy the solution in the real world – with all its complex factors now playing a role. These include environmental factors, end-user behavior, integration and interoperability, and scale.

Often the launch is deployed in phases, starting with a pilot run with a subset of end-users. This is also an important time to ensure financials are tracking to goals and scale as intended.

Ultimately, the solution is launched with marketing, training, and business processes aligned. At this stage, the start-up ingredients are a smaller but still key enabling part of the overall solution. This matters, because it is not about the idea, but rather the idea, plus market fit, plus demonstrated value for the end customer.

The Emerging Power of Platforms

As I stressed at the beginning of this chapter, joining ecosystems is a matter of survival for all industrial companies. That doesn't necessarily also imply building platforms around products. Not every industrial player will pull that off, but the businesses that can will definitely be winners in the Outcome Economy of the future. It is a given that service-driven IIoT platforms, sitting at the heart of wider business ecosystems, will dominate industrial manufacturing in the era of digital. These sprawling and complex business metabolisms will create vast communities and wide-ranging partnerships, extracting value from innovative products and smart services in concert.

The superiority of these business models for industrial companies is palpable. Platforms offer significant operational efficiencies, scalability, and greater innovation quality and speed. They also provide better data insights, leading to better customer experience.

As we speak, around 180 platform companies of global size have already been created. The total value of the companies behind these networks has grown beyond $4.3tn. The trend is moving fast: by 2018 over 50 percent of enterprises are expected to have created or partnered with an industry cloud platform.[4]

Before we delve any deeper into analyzing these complex business structures, let's put some flesh on the bones of what already up-and-running platform products combined with ecosystems can teach industrial manufacturing.

An instructive example is offered by technology giant Apple. Over the years, the Silicon Valley behemoth has come up with a whole string of digital platforms such as the music store iTunes, which disrupted the traditional music industry. Yet the most forward-looking of Apple's platforms has been built around its iPhone mobile device.[5]

What is this platform essentially made of and how does it create value?

One of its most important ingredients is a consumer hardware product designed to find the widest global popularity possible: the iPhone. As of now, over a billion iPhones of different generations have been sold, forming a strong hardware basis for the platform.

The second ingredient is Apple's encouragement of third-party app developers to design and sell software-solutions that can run on the iPhone operating system, addressing numerous aspects of consumers' lives. This has triggered myriad relationships between Apple and a worldwide community of independent software developers. They have so far created two million consumer apps,[6] a number Apple itself would never have been able to reach on its own.

The third component is the App Store, opened by the company in 2008 to offer developers a functioning marketplace for their software creations. The store is not only the place where Apple shares revenues and profits with its platform and ecosystem partners. It is also a tool for the company to supervise the quality and design of proposed apps so that the high global popularity of the iPhone can be kept intact – thus keeping the joint value creation machine running.

What is critical is a powerful consumer-oriented platform literally sucking in knowledge and ingenuity from a vast intellectual catchment area beyond its own parameters, amalgamating it with internal technical brilliance and expertise, producing value and shared profits for all ecosystem partners.

The broadly installed hardware base makes it hugely attractive to third parties to develop apps. And the ever broader supply of apps renders it ever more attractive to consumers to pick the hardware for enjoying them. In that way, the platform literally nourishes itself.

This could be done by industrial enterprises as well.

From Transaction Hubs to Innovation Machines

As we can see from Apple's example, network dynamics and multiplication effects are characteristic for platforms, creating a self-nourishing momentum of growth.

And although not all platforms are purely designed as digital hubs, most of them harness the powerful forces of data-based mass connectivity offered by the Internet. Only the network character allows for the build-up of critical mass as platform users attract one another in ever-increasing waves, thus creating more platform value.

A pure market mechanism stands initially at the center of the most elementary form of platform. All it does is facilitate transactions; the best example is probably online marketplaces such as Amazon or Ebay and a similar mechanism sits at the heart of Chinese e-commerce company Alibaba or the accommodation and transport platforms Airbnb and Uber. Alibaba, Amazon's main rival in China, facilitates 12.7bn orders via its marketplace annually.[7]

If a platform matures beyond that stage, it moves on from a pure transactional role to become an intellectual exchange, the seed for powerful innovation. This is closer to platforms used by industrial manufacturers or indeed Apple's developer platform. This advanced form offers a basis on which innovators exchange and commercialize their propositions for new products and services in a complementary way. Here the platform is embedded in an innovation ecosystem.

The greatest power is achieved when both elements – transactional and intellectual exchange – are put into ideal proportion leading to an integrated platform.

Apple's expansive and highly adaptable halo of software partners has become the role model for other business sectors as software has started to play an ever more important role in industrial products – from cars to planes to kitchen blenders. Software is defining more and more of the market value of such products and gradually giving them the innovative edge.

The dynamic loop just described between platform orchestrator Apple and its ecosystem partners does exactly that. It secures permanent and fast innovation. There is simply no more productive source for novel ideas than the visions of thousands of software-developing enthusiasts and profit-seeking marketers figuring out propositions for a platform product. The aim for any industrial platform creators would be to remain the controlling force and hurdle of approval in this complex ecosystem.

So, a heavy equipment manufacturer catering for the raw materials and commodity sector might invite independent external app entrepreneurs to contribute software solutions that can steer a fleet of its mining trucks or check the load sizes of iron ore cars on a cargo train. Or a mechanical engineering business or a manufacturer of domestic appliances could open up to external software development partners or fellow appliance producers that will inflate value into their own products for shared profits.

It is worth making the more general point that ecosystems are not static. Rather partners come together according to topical needs and strategic priorities. Ecosystems are by nature dynamic and need to be refreshed on an ongoing basis. However, this is one of the benefits of leveraging ecosystems versus building capability in house. You assemble, disassemble, and reassemble capabilities provided by your external partners and matching your needs precisely.

Platforms as "Tissue"

Big industrial manufacturing businesses such as GE or Siemens offer or are working already towards powerful cloud-based platforms for the industrial sector that serve customers and their hardware as a universal software "tissue" from end-to-end.

The market for such software platforms is still in its infancy but will develop quickly. Data collection, monitoring, analytics for decision-making, but also the active control of processes and machinery are the primary functions these platforms will eventually fulfill for their operators.

Thus, sprawling and formerly siloed industrial businesses will for the first time be able to tie together everything happening across all their functions under one roof. This will heighten transparency and operational efficiency by several orders of magnitude.

Predix, for instance, is GE's IIoT platform, its open-architecture operating system for building applications that connect to industrial assets, collect and analyze data, and deliver insights for optimizing industrial infrastructure and operations. Deployed both within GE and across other industrial companies, Predix is designed to play several roles - including integrating manufacturing data end-to-end in GE, enabling customers to learn how to control and maintain the company's equipment more efficiently and effectively, and supporting third parties using Predix for their own products as an IIoT platform of choice.

Thus the system allows supervisors to oversee a complex business organism from the perspective of one single control tower – one with X-ray-like capability when it comes to seeing into the operation's workings. Reaction times are dramatically shortened and maintenance cycles optimized, with the cost benefits being obvious.

There are a few impressive real-life examples already functioning. A fully digitized and largely automated iron ore mine in Latin America is remotely controlled by supervisors sitting at its parent in Australia. Without a data-aggregating industrial software platform, this would be impossible. And again, the cost advantage of such setups is instantly obvious.

The MindSphere platform offered by Siemens fulfills a similar purpose. It is essentially a system of connector boxes that can easily be installed on existing shop-floor infrastructure and machinery. These aggregate the data collected from sensors and machines and send it to the cloud for analytics, visualization, and management decisions.

Such platforms are highly adaptable and can be used on industrial businesses of all scopes or sectors. They could, for instance, be used for running everything from the relatively simple mechanism and service of a baggage belt system at an airport to a large car manufacturer's complex assembly line. Research departments could be connected to the system in the same way as customer service units.

The cloud-based platform, which is offered as a service, is connected to a database. It is therefore highly scalable and heavily geared towards effective data analytics, which pays off when it comes to running cost-effective predictive maintenance schemes.

Other vendors, such as Schneider Electric or Trumpf, have built their own as-a-service industrial platforms and hope to one day create extensive and powerful ecosystems around them. Pure software vendors such as IBM or Microsoft have also joined the industrial platform building fray.

Importantly, platforms such as Predix and MindSphere will eventually come with app stores attached and thus form their own ecosystem of developers and alliance partners. The companies will provide external software architects with all the software documentation necessary to create their own solutions for typical business applications such as data analytics, material flow management tools and location services – all highly tailored and marketable for individual company needs. Essentially, these platforms will gradually pick up Apple's pioneering role model to become the centers of wide-ranging ecosystems.

It will soon be common for industrial engineering firms or heavy equipment makers to set up their own marketplace platforms for their products and related data flows. In a first move, for example, Germany-based concrete pump manufacturer Putzmeister plans to rent out its mobile pumps as well as just selling them.[8]

Product users will share information, allowing all ecosystem partners to benefit, as they find relevant data to optimize set-up times, material usage, and various machine parameters or power consumption patterns, as well as minimizing error sources or downtime triggers.

Users' practical experience, pooled through such platforms, will add value to everyone and could be financially leveraged by the platform organizer through introduction of a paywall.

Three Stages of Maturity

Industry platforms primarily aim at building effective information hubs on which broader intellectually and financially crossfeeding ecosystems can be established. The principal and most important function of such platforms is to spark silo-free network cooperation among partners, the basis for multiplier effects between companies.

Overall we can distinguish three stages of maturity in industrial platforms:

1. Connected product. The starting point for any platform in the industrial sector is a connected product or some form of connected machinery. By being connected and smartened it has cleared the entry hurdle to become a first-level platform product – just like in the case of the Biesse Group highlighted in Chapter 4 – that can carry all sorts of software-driven services – just like the iPhone. The foundation is provided by connected, software-enabled hardware items that are "smart" because they know their own manufacturing and usage history and generate data that is relayed back to its manufacturers where the data feeds into network physical platforms to be analyzed and used for improvement of products and processes. This is the basic entry-stage platform model for all industrial manufacturers. It will be indispensable as the platform economy evolves. Thus smart products will themselves serve also as physical platforms. A car, for example, can act as a node on the Internet, as can a machine in a factory equipped with web-based control.[9]

2. Smart service. The use of platforms provides analytical algorithmic power to filter valuable insights from incoming product data. This is then made available to third-party service providers that can use it to design smart services around the smart hardware produced. At this second level, industrial platforms, normally various machines or products, are linked up and create a degree of collective smartness that allows for both sides of the platform – the provider and the user – to create software-based services.

3. System of systems. This is the final and most advanced stage. These aggregator platforms offer all participants even bigger service opportunities. The crucial point is, that these smart service platforms are no longer tied to physical objects, brands or a specific manufacturer's smart product. They can form standalone businesses in the same way Uber is an independent transport platform with no ownership connection to its original data sources, i.e. independent cab drivers and their cars. In the industrial sector, one could, for instance, imagine a company that organizes all necessary building materials, construction workers, tools, and heavy equipment to be present at the right time at a construction site. Importantly, each new level of aggregation could bring new additional service opportunities.

This three-stage roadmap shows that software-defined platforms will eventually start to integrate heterogeneous physical hardware systems and services into new propositions for the market in industrial manufacturing sectors.

The emergence of software-defined platforms and smart service platforms, including the various online marketplaces and app stores built upon them, and the ecosytems they are embedded in, will be key to competing successfully on the future global market.

Another point worth stressing is that companies will at some point also need to define how they want to play the platform game – as provider or as operator and orchestrator. And how closely do they want to attach the platform to their product – should they open it or rather use it as an additional product-feature and thereby run it more as a proprietary system.

This roadmap also demonstrates how far traditional notions of competition will change in a digitized industrial world. The old business of having a better product proposition on the market becomes barely relevant anymore. In the future, competition is created between rival platform ecosystems and their members and managers – just as already happens between Apple's OS ecosystem and Google's Android empire.

But note: in the industrial sector, the basis for all platform building remains a smart and connected product.

Gently Disassembling to Make Way for New Business Models

Running a platform and its respective ecosystem blurs and moves boundaries – not only within an organization but especially at its outer edges. This will amount, no doubt, to a significant break from traditional company set-ups and management habits.

This requires a special form of migration management. Industrial enterprises need to keep their strength in the traditional core business while making exploratory trips into the digital New.

But how do you build or join an ecosystem aiming at a new business model when your legacy business is necessarily stuck in very vertical and rigid lines of management, plus siloed data and information flows?

It is a matter of gradually opening up, as the graphic below illustrates (Figure 9.2). The aim is to move your total organization from centralized structures for digital strategy and execution to a hybrid and eventually decentralized layout. Ultimately, digital strategy and its execution should be strongly linked to a designated new platform business case, free to join the necessary ecosystem resources it needs to flourish in the New (see Figure 9.2).

It is the main skill of platform business leaders to decide at any given moment on the optimal scope, scale and shape of a platform, the share of value going to different partners and the sanctions that follow misconduct within the ecosystem. It is also about the creation of enough incentives to foster good practice and the alignment of conflicting objectives and strategies among ecosystem allies.

Figure 9.2 – Organizational Set-ups for Making new Business Models Happen[10]

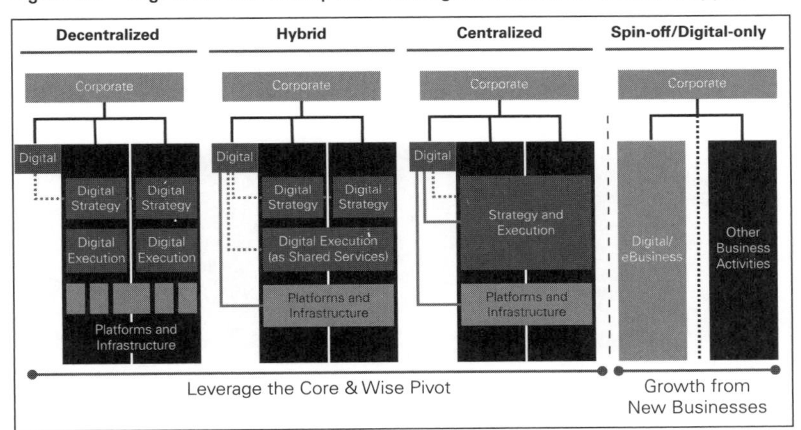

Asset-Heavy vs. Asset-Light

The creation of industrial platforms implies that profits are hunted outside the accustomed product markets in a wider ecosystem market. This divides enterprises into the principal categories of asset-light and asset-heavy.

If you are asset-heavy, for instance an industrial engineering firm with a strong legacy market for your machinery products, you might find it a struggle to quickly accumulate enough organizational capital to run, next to your core hardware products, a fast-growing ecosystem of hundreds of external or semi-external partner developers, hardware suppliers, service subcontractors or customers.

Very asset-light platform operators such as Airbnb or Uber, will in turn often find it difficult to manage bits of the ecosystem they do not fully control. A global accommodation trader such as Airbnb without owned accommodation infrastructure can barely affect the accommodation quality offered by its platform partners, the home owners.

Hence, for the asset-light, the art is to come as close as possible to a hundred percent control by looking beyond software-based matching mechanisms into investments in human talent, values and norms.

Figure 9.3 – Platforms by Entrerprise Type[11]

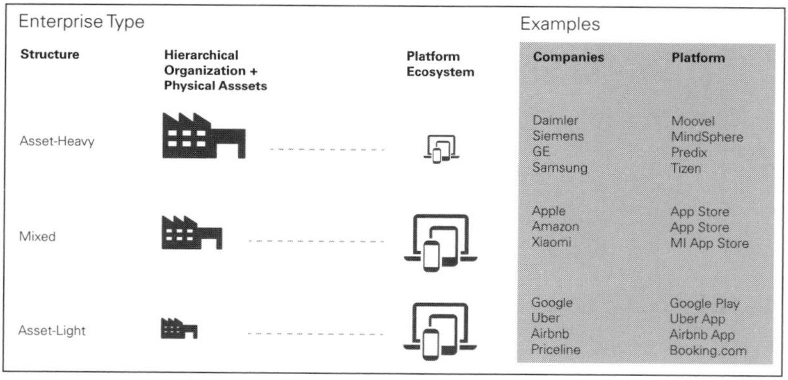

Enterprise Type			Examples	
Structure	**Hierarchical Organization + Physical Asssets**	**Platform Ecosystem**	**Companies**	**Platform**
Asset-Heavy			Daimler Siemens GE Samsung	Moovel MindSphere Predix Tizen
Mixed			Apple Amazon Xiaomi	App Store App Store MI App Store
Asset-Light			Google Uber Airbnb Priceline	Google Play Uber App Airbnb App Booking.com

Most industrial manufacturers, even IT vanguards like Apple, sit somewhere in the middle between asset-light and asset-heavy. Car producers such as Germany's Daimler run traditional car production lines while having invested heavily in car-sharing schemes and other mobility solutions, creating no significant overlap with their core business. For them, the big objective is to keep legacy business in profitable shape while dedicating human and financial resources to novel platforms with changing size and set-up.[12]

Five Things to Watch out for When Building Platforms

Keeping a platform productive requires a management style that innovates the platform itself on an ongoing basis. A platform can only create superior value for partners and customers when it can react and adapt to changing markets or evolving technology.

How can this flexibility be provided in very practical terms?

The following five factors generate the network effects and the critical mass crucial to platform success.

1. Openness. Software platform ecosystems need standardized modules for developers to remain inventive. The use of application programming interfaces (APIs) is in many cases critical for a functioning industrial platform as it is the most reliable way to keep crucial data flowing towards all relevant parties in the ecosystem. API technology allows for work with standardized modules while still guaranteeing a flexible but seamless data flow. This allows a platform to be easily extended by adding additional functionalities quickly. If all developers use a commen API, they can solve problems, tasks, and bugs co-operatively.

Consider the Chinese platform company DHgate.com, a cross-border trading hub for manufacturing businesses wanting to connect with a global customer base. It enables factories to join an ecosystem of standardized services – from logistics and payment to Internet finance and innovation capabilities. Sales-oriented manufacturers benefit through membership from increased margins, a shorter business cycle, extended global reach and strong local language services. Buyers meanwhile enjoy a seamless and secure bulk purchase experience supported by DHgate.com-trained customer service representatives. Such a flexible and effective transaction platform could not exist without a reliable API-based modular approach.[13]

2. Pricing sophistication. While traditional business models may make managers reluctant to give product or services away for free, such practices can be highly successful from a platform perspective. This is especially the case when one side of a market is needed to attract the participation of the other. Due to the extensive information flowing from markets back to platforms, the pricing strategies available on platform businesses differ strikingly from more traditional approaches. There are many more dynamics and real-time elements involved and much more flexibility is possible and required. "Freemium" elements, where a brand offers a bifurcated proposition with paid-for high-end and free low-end product or service elements can easily be implemented. So can pay-as-you-go models, billing just at the exact time a product or service is used, or models of surge pricing where rates adapt to demand minute by minute. Advanced platform businesses are taking this side of their digital operation model to great lengths.

Online auction platform Ebay is of course the obvious example, with real-time auction process one of its core mechanisms. There are also reverse auction specialists such as MyHammer or Vasthouse serving as good examples. But also look at room manager Airbnb. Its algorithms have a built-in real-time system for hiking or lowering room rates according to local demand. Digital platform businesses such as Uber can profit from the flexibility their system offers when it comes to observing, for instance, a regulatory ceiling for taxi rates as is in effect in many emerging countries.[14]

3. Flexibility and agility. A business creating a platform has to have a notion of how big its business could grow and how fast. Platform ecosystems must also be flexible enough to quickly adapt to new trends in the market or promising new entrants to the ecosystem. Agility and scalability, and the awareness of their necessity among relevant managers in the ecosystem, is key. Platforms need to be adaptive enough to accommodate partners that complement products or services, provide payment, as Alipay does for Alibaba, or develop apps. These in turn further improve the power of platforms to scale rapidly and robustly.

4. Personalization. Targeting individuals and organizations across all channels at scale relies on mass personalization. The aim is to understand customer intent, then dynamically and uniquely tailor experiences to each individual and context seamlessly. Amazon uses interest- and intent-collection management tools to encourage buyer "stickiness." Personalization will vary by country or region based on data privacy laws.[15]

5. Cybersecurity. This is key. Customers need to be sure the right safeguards are in place and their privacy is uncompromised. Authentication of community members and their activities is the platform owner and the partners' primary responsibility, far more than in an offline business. Protection of a platform needs to account for both prevention and compensation. Here, platform owners can differentiate themselves. DHgate.com has partnered with Authenticateit for product tracking, anti-counterfeit technology, upgrades to the merchant rating system and an escrow system to build buyers' confidence.[16]

Takeaways

1. Data-driven smart services will shape the New of the industrial world. They will allow for new hyperpersonalized and context-specific user experiences created through the connection of smart products with platform-based services using the power of broad ecosystems.

2. Ecosystems and platforms are becoming innovation and growth engines for most manufacturing enterprises. This change will be fast, disruptive and redefine the rules of competitiveness.

3. Hold on to your data. In a data-driven economy, it becomes a product in itself – one with immense value.

4. Ecosystem yourself. Competition between products and companies will be replaced by competition between fluid digital platform-driven ecosystems. Start connecting your enterprise and products to the outside.

5. Anticipate and lead from the front in the move towards an ecoystem. Setting up partner ecosystems and embedding your organization in them takes time, cuts through the organization and implies a profound change in mindset. It will not happen by itself.

PART III

The Future is Now and Tomorrow

Chapter 10

A Visionary Outlook – The Digital Industrial Enterprise

Our society, and with it our economy and industries, is undergoing a fundamental shift towards an intensely digitized lifestyle. This ground-breaking jolt, born on the back of technological quantum leaps, will represent the new normal for quite some time, for us as individuals and for businesses. Spectacular new technologies will keep leaping off the drawing boards, transforming the way we live, work, communicate, invent and make things over the next decades. The industrial sector will witness the breaking of technological sound barriers and drastic changes to operational models. As per the analysis of this book, the sector will depart from its focus on physical products, shifting towards selling service-based outcomes, an operational model that will have become mainstream in many of the markets across the world around 2030. As I have stressed, businesses should make positive use of this early momentum. They should start laying digital ground works and accumulate experience and expertise today to prepare for the Outcome Economy of tomorrow. But it is also worthwhile to look beyond that. Thus, I will end this book by describing the world businesses should be preparing for, leaping even farther into the future to see how the years 2030 and beyond will look.

Over the course of this book we have touched on remarkable technology pushes, shifts and trends preparing industrial businesses for their wholesale digitization, including drastically changed operational models. We hoped to deliver to business leaders a feel for the unbridled flywheel power digital technology will bring to industrial value creation and business model innovation in the decades to come.

We analyzed and emphasized manifold overlapping streaks of breakthroughs in microelectronics and software programming, in cloud computing and mobile connectivity, in sensor technology and business analytics, in artificial intelligence and computer processing power.

We emphasized that all these individual technology threads are about to combine to bring about a change the size of which industrial businesses have not seen in the history of modern manufacturing.

We also showed how price erosion sits at the heart of the mass deployment of these novel technologies, fueling the relentless expansion of the Industrial Internet of Things (IIoT).

Finally, we highlighted that businesses, workers and customers in the industrial sector are all adopting a novel form of industrial consumerism valuing the experience with a product or service above everything else.

Let's take a last glimpse at the impressive technological groundswell our civilization is traveling on, reminding ourselves of some of its most stunning yardsticks. The processing power of an iPhone is today on par with the fastest supercomputer available in 1975. Buying that power would have cost you $5m back then, while it comes to you for a mere $400 today. The server performance you can buy for a dollar today will have doubled in only 18 months' time, the number of industrial machines connected via advanced data networks has increased by 300 percent over just five years while the number of industrial robots has grown at a rate of around 170 percent over the last three years.

If we assume that that rate of change continues over the next decades, we will, according to the American IT historian and futurist Ray Kurzweil, be able to buy a computer device as powerful as the combined intelligence of all human brains for the price of a refrigerator in 2050.[1] Way before that, within the next decade, Kurzweil expects machines to fully master natural language and text, understanding, reading and acting on it indistinguishably from humans.

It is hardly any wonder that these trends are not only driving a broad wave of digitization in our industries but will also further radically transform day-to-day life and work across all their functions – from shop floors to boardrooms.

Clearly, mere server capacity and processing speed will not be a bottleneck. Built on a supply of practically limitless computing power, the IIoT will be very real and fully brought to life by ubiquitous software acting as a connecting "tissue" for the sprawling industrial metabolisms and business networks of the second machine age. Ecosystem borders at enterprise or even nation state levels will only be faintly delineated and highly porous.

In the Pull Economy, Meet the Production Crowd

A flavor of what this distant future will hold, can be studied in some pioneer businesses today.

Take printer producer Hewlett Packard`s HP Instant Ink scheme, an ink cartridge replacement service. You simply register your HP Instant Ink eligible printer to for an Instant Ink plan. As a connected, sensorized hardware item, the printer sends ink level information to HP. When the machine runs low, replacement cartridges are shipped to you. HP charges you based on your usage levels.[2]

Clearly this works for a big office with 120 printers producing hundreds of pages per day just as well as for a single freelancer printing 11 pages a month. It covers all customer segments via scalable technology at a stroke.

This is manufacturing sector reality today. It's a relatively modest example, but hints at how a fully developed Pull Economy decades down the line will eventually look across all industry sectors. Customers will receive hyperpersonalized, administratively lean services from providers that spring into action on an ad hoc basis in response to individual demand.

This will be the dominant theme in the industrial sector in the year 2030. Industrial goods such as machinery or trucks will be created largely to meet instant demand, delivered just in time, often through decentralized technologies such as 3D Printing, and sourced from free-floating production ensembles and ecosystems of transitory business partners.

By then the concept of the preceding Outcome Economy, discussed in this book, will be every business leader's default strategy. The need to provide customers with outcomes, not just hardware to achieve outcomes on their own, will be part of the entry-level syllabus at any business school in 2030.

This entails the recognition that only software-enabled and sophisticated hardware products can promise outcomes such as the guarantee of 2,860 engine hours, made by an engine maker to an airline, or a truck manufacturer's pledge to a mining operator to provide everything necessary for the movement of 4,500 tonnes of iron ore from an inland mine to a harbour for shipping.

Ownership of products will go down entirely new paths in the Pull Economy. The company from which I buy the outcome of a warm home will own my air conditioner and negotiate with the power company when it is supposed to operate. It will specify the device and outsource its manufacturing to the lowest bidder while tracking its behavior across its lifecycle. All this will be in response to my usage needs and patterns – the pull.

The push economy – today's mainstream business model, dominant for practically the whole history of modern capitalism – tries to assess demand in advance and responds by designing a standardized hardware item such as a car or an electric razor, which is then pushed into an anonymous market via standardized marketing and distribution methods. The Pull Economy will organize its workings the other way around. Customer demand – the pull – will call the shots. But via advanced algorithmic sensing relying on a multitude of installed sensors in the field, this demand will be sensed even before customers themselves are aware of it.

In addition to this, the Pull Economy is characterized by the ability to instantly test ideas on concepts in real-time, and also to propose personalized products in real-time and on the basis of tailored one-to-one marketing.

If this sounds like magical mindreading, consider some of existing innovations that, while impressive, are just the Pull Economy's baby steps: a shop mirror fitted with Microsoft's recognition software and AI to analyze body language can now judge the likelihood of a sale; algorithms can sense general trends among the population, and even create or contribute to the creation of blockbuster books and TV shows. From this standpoint, customers lose personal ownership of their own demand.

This, in turn, will allow for seamless end-to-end automated supply and production chains for many industrial products.

This will eventually be a world in which industrial businesses act strictly along open, flexible, modular, loosely coupled industrial provision ecosystems that use and coordinate a whole crowd of stacked specialized businesses from a broad range of sectors and regions.

It will also be the rise of the "composite business" that assembles industrially made items in smaller, specialized units that can come together on demand. Again, some pioneering companies are already operating like this. In the UK, service provider RPD International, takes care of big companies' manufacturing and development processes. You deliver an idea and RPD designs, prototypes and manufactures the product through their global contract manufacturer network. They even distribute it for you.[3]

In the Pull Economy, then, demand can ultimately create instantaneous transitory work alliances for "lot ones" that then dissolve back into a more generic network, standing by for the next production call. Shop floors, back offices, R&D units, supply chains, marketing teams, subcontractors, and ecosystem partners are all effectively interlinked and digitally connected so that a customer can get a hyperpersonalized industrial item at a few mouse clicks from a free-wheeling halo of rapidly reconfiguring providers – ultra-localized and personalized.

So industrial manufacturing will be a rapid, on-the-fly process. Customer loyalties will have lost traction for many medium-sized industrial businesses while others – a happy few larger industrial players – will even acquire more brand weight.[4]

These will be the big winners in tomorrow's Pull Economy, the ones who are able to set up and run such complex multi-dimensional networks, placing themselves at the centre of potent ecosystems enabling outcomes.

Technology Makes Making More Flexible

It is obvious how digital technology will have a pivotal, enabling role in this economy. The digital-physical blur we are experiencing in its infancy today will be hugely intensified over the next two decades.

An emerging new layer of connected intelligence will become ever more palpable and will augment our actions as working individuals, automate processes we work in and incorporate digitally empowered machines into our work lives – increasing our insight into and control over the tangible world.

Every bit of technology described in this book will still feature significantly in the Pull Economy of 2040 and beyond, but will take a much more sophisticated position in industrial production, more embedded in products, operations, customer, interactions, and workforces.

At the core of industrial markets will be Living Products, so enabled by software to respond to and anticipate human needs that they will come across as "brothers in mind" to users. These will be mainstream in industrial markets and, hyper-connected, will form a strong link between manufacturer and customer.

Maker and buyer connectedness means it will no longer be possible to localize manufacturing definitively in a factory plant. Instead, multiple process arrangements will dominate the Pull Economy, formed ad hoc by competition dynamics and individual customer preferences.

Think of the thousands of spare parts a 2030 car manufacturer would need for its vintage vehicle series. It would have numerous options for sourcing these: a company could plan centrally and produce parts locally after a customer has placed an order. Another might offer desktop manufacturing, designing parts bespoke for the customer to produce, perhaps on his or her own local 3D Printer. Alternatively again, the customer might design the parts on a manufacturing platform for a company to produce and ship. Or, in a fourth scenario, open manufacturing, the customer would design and produce parts locally, from blueprints provided by the company.

Industrial manufacturing on shop floors will have similarly changed by 2040. Fast prototyping, mass customization, delocalization and rapid manufacturing will be the norm across a much more scattered industrial landscape than today's. Industrial customers will get a prototype within a week where it previously took six months.

As all this efficiency kicks in, unit prices will drop, triggering a surge in the affordability and hence demand for more personalized services and outcomes. With asset and resource utilization also increasing as a typical element of these developments, all this creates substantial upside for consumers and businesses – in a more sustainable fashion that is possible today.

Today's mobile phone manufacturing cluster in China's Shenzhen area might be a precursor of what is to come. Ad hoc manufacturers there will build a cell phone that looks like a car key or your house and get it to you in just in a few days.

Even today's mass-products such as cars will have enough flexibility built into the processes that create them to be highly customizable. Instead of giant, purpose-built plants supplying the global market, smaller, regionalized plants responding more rapidly to local demand will be the order of the day.

But the industrial platforms discussed throughout this book will still be a pronounced feature of the Pull Economy two decades down the line. Hardware will sit at the core of a swirling developer community, coding apps and software to bring it to life via various applications.

What has been pioneered by Apple and its iPhone, will be the norm for many industrial products. Platform hardware will form the nucleus of the most powerful ecosystems in the Pull Economy.

Weaker ecosystems will still enjoy a healthy life without a platform product at its core, but every industrial business will one way or another be part of an ecosystem by 2030. It will be a precondition for survival. The major platform and ecosystem orchestrators will not all be old industrial brand names. Disruptive new contenders will be able to slip in with a nimble start-up model. There is no reason to doubt that an Uber-style service could work in the industrial sphere.

Edge or "fog" computing will be big as well, as connectivity will probably not be able to keep pace with the massive amounts of industrial data produced and sent to central server hubs for analysis and automated process control. The software-as-a-service concept, though, will be standard throughout the industrial sector as no carmaker, heavy equipment manufacturer or utility will run its own server farms anymore, but will send data into the cloud for storage and processing.

Devices to pick up signals and voice, and wireless machine sensors and wearables will be greatly advanced by ever-improved battery life. Right now, universal power supplies, wireless charging, charging surfaces, solar and kinetic chargers, fuel cells, and biofuel for mobile devices are being rapidly developed and scaled to meet growing device power needs and improve energy efficiency.

The industrial robot will be so advanced that huge factories will be run at unprecedented productivity levels with only a small group of highly skilled supervisors roaming the shop floors and control towers. The few machine operators on site will be augmented by software-driven eyewear and body-worn technology of all kinds to compensate for the natural weakness of their eyesight, hearing and musculature.

Cobots – collaborative robots – will also be seen across business functions and R&D and customer service units will accommodate them as productivity enhancing colleagues in significant numbers. We reckon that a minimum of 30 to 40 percent of industrial jobs will be cobotized by 2030 in one form or another. White-collar cobot algorithms will even be board members.

The huge advances in automated process optimization, wearable computing, machine learning and context-aware services will have palpable ramifications for management tasks. Middle-ranking managers will be a dying breed as software algorithms initially developed for crowdsourcing and social enterprise applications become able to perform task assignment and coordination roles traditionally occupied by human supervisors – and supersede them. In its day-to-day life, the enterprise of 2030 and beyond will operate with highly sophisticated predictive enabling tools.

Reflecting the Internet's trajectory in general, voice, haptics, and gestures will dominate the next era of human-machine interfaces inside and outside businesses. Responsive and anticipatory systems will leverage implicit intention markers such as eye tracking, emotional signals, and other non-verbal cues. Our minds will literally be read by collaborative computers.

The enabling technologies for this will be multisensory interfaces, augmented reality and smarter touchscreen surfaces. Body sensor implants that can read intention are already in the making. They will be major features once fully digitized industrial engineering and manufacturing are up and running.[5]

Machines will be much more intimately tied into our lives by sensors and data flows. These technologies will leverage all our human senses to become much more intuitive and even invisible. Thus we will also witness the interplay between people, machines, platforms and broader smart systems such as in transportation, healthcare, safety and cities. Our domestic air purifiers or cars, for example, will be linked to public pollution information in parallel with our health monitors. Bridges and roads will become smart and interact with individual traffic participants.

We have stressed in this book how important software will be as the dominant value creator for future producers and users. Given software's rapid progress today, think how far it will have progressed by 2030. It will be vital for you as an industrial manufacturer and service provider to keep hardware and software in close sync. Essentially the goal will be to accelerate the hardware cycle to catch up to the speed of software development and give industrial goods a more software-like existence.

There will be ever more symbiosis between hardware and software, each adapting to keep pace with the other. This will be possible because hardware will be as updateable as software, thanks to materials that can easily change shape or alter physical properties like conductivity.

Finally, on the back of cloud supercomputing, dynamic, virtualized network architectures and cognitive computing, the Internet, including its industrial cousin the IIoT, will release itself from its creators' intentions and develop its own mind in unexpected and transformative ways.

This is the point, for instance, where enterprises turn into self-organizing entities only remotely controlled from outside, or when ecosystems start to develop their own mind when deciding on capacity for and delivery of a customer outcome.

Algorithms will harness massive data to generate meaningful patterns of human and machine behavior. But they will also create emergent and volatile properties as they change their own codes in order to compete against other algorithms.

Finally, the combination of Living Products, hyperpersonalization and highly flexible production facilities will also change the industrial landscape, accelerating the reshoring trend, where much smaller automated factories will be relocated much closer to end customers. The notion of global will be replaced by the "me economy".

In such an environment, network architecture will be deliberately engineered to take advantage of neural network decision-making. Networks will be wired together with formations designed to privilege certain connection pathways over others.

The Pull Economy will be, by definition, a world of rapid action. So, whatever hardware product or service you want to bring to market, organize for maximum modularity, including in your supply chain. Embed yourself in the Pull Economy and work out whether you are an orchestrator or supplier in it.

Always start with a software mindset and a customer need in mind and assume you can build anything, or at least a testable prototype, in just a few weeks. Make the user experience the top of your strategic agenda and assume you will be tied to your product in some way until it is recycled. Design your product for low-cost manufacturing, but make it easy to customize based on market preferences, and assume very short lifecycles but extensive recycling.

Nothing as Usual Becomes Business as Usual

As this short, kaleidoscopic tour indicates, digital industry's Big Bang has effectively just happened. Its universe will be expanding for quite sometime – certainly well beyond 2030.

But even this perpetual change implies a constant. In 2030, the rules for pursuing the digital New will still hold true: start small, see what works, then scale. Be adaptive, experimental, and curious. Install agile hierarchies and think outside the walls of your legacy products, siloes, company, sector, and markets.

Above all, continue to grow your core business to manage the pivot to the New.

Why will you still be pivoting to the New in 2030? Because the New is, by definition, always changing, so your pivoting must go on and on. When you complete a pivot, start again. The core from which you pivot will be your old New and you must pivot to the new New – then pivot again.

For now, clearly, this is a story with no foreseeable end.

After all, in an expanding universe, you also need to keep growing, don't you?

Chapter Takeaways at a Glance

Takeaways Chapter 1 – Industry's Ongoing and Accelerating Digital Transformation

1. The industrial sphere is undergoing a profound, even dramatic change. Its drivers are many, among them the pervasiveness of connected technology, platforms and data optimization, hyper-personalization, and as-a-service business models. And we are just at the beginning of the change.

2. Tightly connected industrial manufacturing processes are going to go mainstream soon. The Industrial Internet of Things (IIoT), will digitally orchestrate factory floors, physical products, workers and more, unleashing enormous value.

3. Critical to success in this new digital industrial world will be the deployment of the right technology, preparation of the digital workforce, intelligent orchestration of both, and embedding of enterprises in the right ecosystems of business partners.

Takeaways Chapter 2 – How the IIoT Leads to the Outcome Economy

1. The Industrial Internet of Things (IIoT) will drastically change the way companies work internally, work with each other, and sell to customers.

2. This will lead to "the end of the product" and the rise of a new kind of economy, the Outcome Economy (or "usage economy"). In this new world, tried-and-tested industrial hardware products are not only eclipsed by their much more profitable service qualities, the user experience and the ecosystems they operate in: They are also commerzialized on a per outcome basis. It is the combination of living products and as-a-service business model that make the outcome economy.

3. This will be the era in which industrial companies move away from rigid business silos to more agile ecosystems and alliances with surprising partners. It they don't, they won't survive in the long run.

Takeaways Chapter 3 – Digital Super Value – A Guiding Light for Digital Strategy

1. Business as usual is over. Manufacturing companies can reap huge immediate and future financial rewards from digitizing their whole value chain. Society as a whole will also massively benefit via enterprises' external value spread.

2. Understanding value is critical for an industrial business in devising a digitization strategy. Different values accrue from digitizing at different speeds. Different functions in different industrial sectors contain digital value pools of widely varying depth.

3. Although new digital business models have yet to deliver on their promise, only those companies investing ahead of existing and emerging competitors will capture the potential and establish leadership.

Takeaways Chapter 4 – Six "No-Regret" Capabilities – the Journey Towards Digital, Mapped out Simply

1. Digitally transforming your company is a challenging task that may look like a scary upheaval of all functions.

2. No perfect or predefined roadmap exists, but that doesn't mean to do nothing. Figuring out the perfect and detailed roadmap for your company is near to impossible and of little value. Set the high-level directions for your company and dive in.

3. Start-up style rapid experimentation is the way to go. The rule of "deploy if successful, move on to the next idea if not" is standard in these firms. There should ideally be multiple rapid-experimentation sites across your enterprise to get the digital ball rolling.

4. There are six core "no-regret" capabilities to be targeted for the first steps towards a full-blown IIoT-powered enterprise: synchronizing the lifecycle clocks, embedding software intelligence and connectivity, using data analytics, rendering manufacturing facilities agile, understanding business as a service, creating and running smart ecosystems.

5. Try out each of these six "no-regret" capabilities and then combine. The benefits will only increase as you do so. This will contribute to quick wins and long-term success.

Takeaways Chapter 5 – Zoom in: How to Make Data Analytics Work Your Way

1. Data and the operational and commercial insights extracted from it are going to be the lifeblood of the industrial sector in the 21st century.

2. All companies have a wealth of unleveraged legacy data. Enriching this data will drive significant value in five main areas: (a) customer experience, (b) product performance, (c) workforce efficiency, (d) operational efficiency, and (e) portfolio optimization of new products and services.

3. Start progressively exploiting operational data hidden in your existing IT systems. Once the first pilots have delivered value, integrate external data. As your products become smarter and more connected, make the direct link.

4. Launch small, safe analytics pilots focused on specific use cases. Do so in as many areas of your company as possible and scale your data platform as soon as success clicks in.

5. Set up a cross-enterprise analytics capability to support all these initiatives within your company. Leverage data analytics service providers to accelerate the process and run pilots targeting both top-line and bottom-line opportunities.

Takeaways Chapter 6 – Zoom in: How to Handle Digital Product Development

1. The entire process chain around developing and designing industrially manufactured items is redefined by the emergence of the smart and connected product.

2. Strengthen your software capabilities – There will be more and more software embedded in your products. Software-enabled services and user experience will be critical, you need to build at pace your software capabilities.

3. A robust Digital Product Lifecycle Management (DPLM) must be the starting point for product development in the emerging era of data-driven Living Products. Set up the right DPLM capabilities: agility, scalability, software intelligence, and unified data connectedness.

4. Synchronize, but do not lock together, the two clocks – and ensure that marketing optimizes the resulting propositions and improvements with regard to the customer.

5. End-to-end. Let your DPLM run through your whole business and become its DNA.

Takeaways Chapter 7 – Zoom in: How to Create a Connected Industrial Workforce

1. The industrial worker of the future will be a data-based decision-maker and supervisory presence on the factory floor, in the engineering centers or on the field servicing products.

2. All business roles and functions will be affected as cobots and artificial intelligence will permeate the enterprise resulting in a blended workforce from the shop floor to the boardroom.

3. Don't wait – proactively manage this revolutionary change in your company.

4. Craft new training and recruitment strategies now – start-up skilling your workforce and recruiting the talent now as the right

skills will be in short supply. Explore new digital workforce models such as crowdsourcing.

5. Focus on your line managers, they will be critical in seeding and steering the change of your entire workforce while undergoing significant changes themselves.

Takeaways Chapter 8 – Zoom in: How to Master Innovation in the New

1. Experience beats product. Improved customer experience is where companies in the industrial sector have seen the greatest success from innovation in recent years.

2. New approaches to innovation can drive significant financial returns especially in sectors such as industrial equipment, consumer goods and consumer electronics.

3. Most industrial companies have very similar innovation investment profiles. The difference comes from the "how" rather than the "what."

4. Open up to the outside. A new view of competitors and the ability to work in more open and fluid ecosystems are key.

5. Brilliant Innovators are solution-centered, powered by insights, drive pivotal leadership and operate at multiple speeds.

Takeaways Chapter 9 – Zoom in: How to Make the Most of Platforms and Ecosystems

1. Data-driven smart services will shape the New of the industrial world. They will allow for new hyperpersonalized and context-specific user experiences created through the connection

of smart products with platform-based services using the power of broad ecosystems.

2. Ecosystems and platforms are becoming innovation and growth engines for most manufacturing enterprises. This change will be fast, disruptive and redefine the rules of competitiveness.

3. Hold on to your data. In a data-driven economy, it becomes a product in itself – one with immense value.

4. Ecosystem yourself. Competition between products and companies will be replaced by competition between fluid digital platform-driven ecosystems. Start connecting your enterprise and products to the outside.

5. Anticipate and lead from the front in the move towards an ecoystem. Setting up partner ecosystems and embedding your organization in them takes time, cuts through the organization and implies a profound change in mindset. It will not happen by itself.

Glossary of Terms

A

AI Artificial Intelligence
ALM Application Lifecycle Management
API Application Programme Interface
AR Augmented Reality

B

B2B Business to Business
B2C Business to Consumer
bn Billion
BOM Bills of Materials

C

CAD Computer-Aided Design
CAGR Compound Annual Growth Rate
CAPEX Capital Expenditure
CD Consumer Durables
CGS Consumer Goods and Services
CIO Chief Information Officer
COSP Customer-Oriented Sales and Production
CPG Consumer Packaged Goods
CRM Customer Relationship Management
CT Control Tower

D

DIPI Digital Industry Performance Index
DNA Deoxyribonucleic Acid
DPL Digital Product Lifecycle
DPLM Digital Product Lifecycle Management
DSF Digital Service Factory

E

EAM Enterprise Asset Management
EB Exabyte = 1000^6 bytes
EBIT Earnings Before Interest and Taxes
EBITDA Earnings Before Interest Payment, Taxes, Depreciation, and Amortization
EBS E-Business Suite
EDI Electronic Data Interchange
EOQ Economic Order Quantity
EOL End of Life
ERP Enterprise Resource Planning

G

GDP Gross Domestic Product
GPS Global Positioning System

H

HCE Heavy Construction Equipment
HR Human Ressources

I

IEE Industrial & Electrical Equipment Manufacturers
IIoT Industrial Internet of Things

IoT	Internet of Things
IPO	Incubator Program Office
IPR	Intellectual Property Rights
IT	Information Technology

K

km	Kilometer
KPI	Key Performance Indicator

L

LS	Life Science
LTE	Long Term Evolution

M

m	Million
M2M	Machine to Machine
MES	Manufacturing Execution Systems
Mfg	Manufacturing
MOQ	Multiple Order Quantity
MR	Mixed Reality
MVP	Minimum Viable Product

N

NFC	Near Field Communication

O

OEM	Original Equipment Manufacturer
OES	Original Equipment Supplier
OI	Operating Income
OPEX	Operating Expenses
OS	Operating System
OT	Operational Technology

P

PC	Personal Computer
PDM	Product Data Management
PLM	Product Lifecycle Management
POS	Point of Sale
PRD	Product
pts	Points

R

R&D	Research and Development
ROI	Return on Investment

S

SME	Small and Medium Enterprises
SW	Software

T

tn	Trillion
TV	Television

U

US	United States
UAS	Unmanned Aircraft Systems
UK	United Kingdom
UX	User Experience

V

VR	Virtual Reality

W

WEF	World Economic Forum

Endnotes

Preface

1 http://www.gartner.com/newsroom/id/3165317, accessed January 15, 2017

2 World Economic Forum, "Deep Shift: Technology Tipping Points and Societal Impact," September 2015. http://www3.weforum.org/docs/WEF_GAC15_Technological_Tipping_Points_report_2015.pdf

3 Accenture, "Intelligent Automation: The essential new co-worker for the digital age," 2016. https://www.accenture.com/fr-fr/_acnmedia/PDF-11/Accenture-Intelligent-Automation-Technology-Vision-2016-france.pdf

4 http://www.mining-technology.com/features/featurerio-tinto-rolling-out-the-worlds-first-fully-driverless-mines-4831021/, accessed January 26, 2017

Introduction

1 Accenture Research

2 World Economic Forum White Paper, in collaboration with Accenture, "Industrial Internet of Things: Unleashing the Potential of Connected Products and Services," January 2015. http://www3.weforum.org/docs/WEFUSA_IndustrialInternet_Report2015.pdf

Chapter 1

1 Accenture, "Driving Unconventional Growth through the Industrial Internet of Things," 2015. https://www.accenture.com/za-en/_acnmedia/Accenture/next-gen/reassembling-industry/pdf/Accenture-Driving-Unconventional-Growth-through-IIoT.pdf

2 © Accenture, based on: http://rethinkresearch.biz/articles/intels-end-to-end-iot-message-is-strong-but-quark-is-a-gamble-2/, accessed February 1, 2017; Cisco, "The Internet of Things - How the Next Evolution of the Internet Is Changing Everything," April 2011. http://www.cisco.com/c/dam/en_us/about/ac79/docs/innov/IoT_IBSG_0411FINAL.pdf; GSM Association, "The Mobile Economy 2014". http://www.gsma.com/mobileeconomy/archive/GSMA_ME_2014.pdf; https://www.mashery.com/blog/api-match-maker-developer-connect, accessed February 1, 2017; http://www.usability247.com/blog/making-app-top-usability/, accessed February 1, 2017; Ericsson, "Ericsson Mobility Report," June 2016.

https://www.ericsson.com/assets/local/mobility-report/documents/2016/ericsson-mobility-report-june-2016.pdf

3 © Accenture, based on: The Goldman Sachs Group, Inc., "The Internet of Things: Making sense of the next mega-trend," September 2014. http://www.goldmansachs.com/our-thinking/outlook/internet-of-things/iot-report.pdf; http://www.mkomo.com/cost-per-gigabyte-update, accessed February 3, 2017

4 World Economic Forum White Paper, in collaboration with Accenture, "Industrial Internet of Things: Unleashing the Potential of Connected Products and Services," January 2015. http://www3.weforum.org/docs/WEFUSA_IndustrialInternet_Report2015.pdf

5 World Economic Forum White Paper, in collaboration with Accenture, "Industrial Internet of Things: Unleashing the Potential of Connected Products and Services," January 2015. http://www3.weforum.org/docs/WEFUSA_IndustrialInternet_Report2015.pdf

6 World Economic Forum White Paper, in collaboration with Accenture, "Digital Transformation of Industries – Demystifying Digital and Securing $100 Trillion for Society and Industry by 2025," January 2015. http://reports.weforum.org/digital-transformation/wp-content/blogs.dir/94/mp/files/pages/files/wef1601-digitaltransformation-1401.pdf

7 Accenture Research

8 © Accenture

9 Accenture, "Driving Unconventional Growth through the Industrial Internet of Things," 2015. https://www.accenture.com/za-en/_acnmedia/Accenture/next-gen/reassembling-industry/pdf/Accenture-Driving-Unconventional-Growth-through-IIoT.pdf

10 Accenture Research

11 Accenture, "Machine Dreams Making the most of the Connected Industrial Workforce," 2016. https://www.accenture.com/t20160506T052209__w__/us-en/_acnmedia/PDF-13/Accenture-Connected-Industrial-Workforce-Research.pdf#zoom=50

12 Accenture, in collaboration with The Economist Intelligence Unit, "From Productivity to Outcomes – Using the Internet of Things to drive future business strategies", 2015. https://www.accenture.com/t00010101T000000__w__/gb-en/_acnmedia/Accenture/Conversion-Assets/DotCom/Documents/Global/PDF/Dualpub_11/Accenture-Industrial-Internet-of-Things-CEO-Briefing-Report-2015.ashx

13 © Accenture

14 http://www.datasciencecentral.com/profiles/blogs/that-s-data-science-airbus-puts-10-000-sensors-in-every-single, accessed January 15, 2017

15 http://www.aerospacemanufacturinganddesign.com/article/millions-of-data-points-flying-part2-121914/, accessed February 1, 2017

16 http://www.history.com/this-day-in-history/ford-motor-company-unveils-the-model-t, accessed January 24, 2017

17 © Accenture

18 World Economic Forum White Paper, in collaboration with Accenture, "Digital Transformation of Industries: Automotive Industry," January 2016. https://www.accenture.com/t20160505T044104__w__/us-en/_acnmedia/PDF-16/Accenture- wef-Dti-Automotive-2016.pdf

Chapter 2

1 © Accenture

2 Barclays, "Disruptive Mobility – A Scenario for 2040...," 2015. https://www.investmentbank.barclays.com/content/dam/barclayspublic/docs/investment-bank/global-insights/barclays-disruptive-mobility-pdf-120115-459kb.pdf

3 © Accenture

4 © Accenture

5 http://www.bbc.co.uk/news/technology-29551380, accessed December 8, 2016

6 http://www.proteus.com/discover/, accessed December 8, 2016

7 World Economic Forum, in collaboration with Accenture, "Digital Transformation of Industries: Digital Enterprise," January 2016. http://reports.weforum.org/digital-transformation/wp-content/blogs.dir/94/mp/files/pages/files/digital-enterprise-narrative-final-january-2016.pdf

8 http://www.philips.com/a-w/about/news/archive/standard/news/press/2015/20150416-Philips-provides-Light-as-a-Service-to-Schiphol-Airport.html, accessed December 8, 2016

9 World Economic Forum, in collaboration with Accenture, "Industrial Internet of Things: Unleashing the Potential of Connected Products and Services," January 2015. http://www3.weforum.org/docs/WEFUSA_IndustrialInternet_Report2015.pdf

10 Accenture, "Driving Unconventional Growth through the Industrial Internet of Things," 2015. https://www.accenture.com/za-en/_acnmedia/Accenture/next-gen/reassembling-industry/pdf/Accenture-Driving-Unconventional-Growth-through-IIoT.pdf

11 Accenture, "Driving Unconventional Growth through the Industrial Internet of Things," 2015. https://www.accenture.com/za-en/_acnmedia/Accenture/next-gen/reassembling-industry/pdf/Accenture-Driving-Unconventional-Growth-through-IIoT.pdf

12 © Accenture, based on: https://www.cbinsights.com/blog/startups-unbundling-fedex/, accessed January 31, 2017

13 World Economic Forum, in collaboration with Accenture, "Industrial Internet of Things: Unleashing the Potential of Connected Products and Services," January 2015. http://www3.weforum.org/docs/WEFUSA_IndustrialInternet_Report2015.pdf

14 Accenture, based on "Embedded Software – The Foundation of New- and Unconventional Growth in Automotive and Industrial Equipment," 2015. https://www.accenture.com/t20150929T015349__w__/us-en/_acnmedia/Accenture/Conversion-Assets/DotCom/Documents/Global/PDF/Dualpub_20/Accenture-AIIT-Embedded-Software-Brochure-Final.pdf

15 Accenture Research

16 https://newsroom.accenture.com/news/accenture-and-siemens-complete-formation-of-omnetric-group-a-joint-venture-focused-on-smart-grid-solutions.htm, accessed January 27, 2017

17 Accenture, "Embedded Software – The Foundation of New- and Unconventional Growth in Automotive and Industrial Equipment," 2015. https://www.accenture.com/t20150929T015349__w__/us-en/_acnmedia/Accenture/Conversion-Assets/DotCom/Documents/Global/PDF/Dualpub_20/Accenture-AIIT-Embedded-Software-Brochure-Final.pdf

18 World Economic Forum, in collaboration with Accenture, "Digital Transformation of Industries: Digital Enterprise," January 2016. http://reports.weforum.org/digital-transformation/wp-content/blogs.dir/94/mp/files/pages/files/digital-enterprise-narrative-final-january-2016.pdf

19 Accenture, "Embedded Software – The Foundation of New- and Unconventional Growth in Automotive and Industrial Equipment," 2015. https://www.accenture.com/t20150929T015349__w__/us-en/_acnmedia/Accenture/Conversion-Assets/DotCom/Documents/Global/PDF/Dualpub_20/Accenture-AIIT-Embedded-Software-Brochure-Final.pdf

Chapter 3

1 © Accenture

2 World Economic Forum White Paper, in collaboration with Accenture, "Digital Transformation of Industries – Demystifying Digital and Securing $100 Trillion for Society and Industry by 2025," January 2016. http://reports.weforum.org/digital-transformation/wp-content/blogs.dir/94/mp/files/pages/files/wef1601-digitaltransformation-1401.pdf

3 © Accenture

4 World Economic Forum White Paper, in collaboration with Accenture, "Digital Transformation of Industries – Demystifying Digital and Securing $100 Trillion

for Society and Industry by 2025," January 2016. http://reports.weforum.org/digital-transformation/wp-content/blogs.dir/94/mp/files/pages/files/wef1601-digitaltransformation-1401.pdf

5 World Economic Forum White Paper, in collaboration with Accenture, "Digital Transformation of Industries – Demystifying Digital and Securing $100 Trillion for Society and Industry by 2025," January 2016. http://reports.weforum.org/digital-transformation/wp-content/blogs.dir/94/mp/files/pages/files/wef1601-digitaltransformation-1401.pdf

6 © Accenture, based on: World Economic Forum, in collaboration with Accenture, „Digital Transformation Initiative: The electricity industry: uncovering value through digital transformation," June 2016. https://www.accenture.com/t20170112T131417__w__/us-en/_acnmedia/Accenture/Conversion-Assets/WEF/PDF/Accenture-Electricity-Industry-slideshare.pdf#zoom=50; World Economic Forum, in collaboration with Accenture, „Digital Transformation Initiative: Reinventing the wheel: digital transformation in the automotive industry," June 2016. https://www.accenture.com/t20170112T131415__w__/us-en/_acnmedia/Accenture/Conversion-Assets/WEF/PDF/Accenture-Automotive-Industry-slideshare.pdf#zoom=50; World Economic Forum, in collaboration with Accenture, "The digital transformation of logistics: threat and opportunity," June 2016. https://www.accenture.com/t20170112T131418__w__/us-en/_acnmedia/Accenture/Conversion-Assets/WEF/PDF/Accenture-Logistics-Industry-slideshare.pdf#zoom=50; World Economic Forum, in collaboration with Accenture, Consumer industries: keeping up with 'digital consumers', June 2016. https://www.accenture.com/t20170112T131416__w__/us-en/_acnmedia/Accenture/Conversion-Assets/WEF/PDF/Accenture-Consumer-Industries-slideshare.pdf#zoom=50

7 © Accenture

8 World Economic Forum White Paper, in collaboration with Accenture, "Digital Transformation of Industries – Demystifying Digital and Securing $100 Trillion for Society and Industry by 2025," January 2016. http://reports.weforum.org/digital-transformation/wp-content/blogs.dir/94/mp/files/pages/files/wef1601-digitaltransformation-1401.pdf

9 World Economic Forum White Paper, in collaboration with Accenture, "Digital Transformation of Industries – Demystifying Digital and Securing $100 Trillion for Society and Industry by 2025," January 2016. http://reports.weforum.org/digital-transformation/wp-content/blogs.dir/94/mp/files/pages/files/wef1601-digitaltransformation-1401.pdf

10 World Economic Forum White Paper, in collaboration with Accenture, "Digital Transformation of Industries – Demystifying Digital and Securing $100 Trillion for Society and Industry by 2025," January 2016. http://reports.weforum.org/digital-transformation/wp-content/blogs.dir/94/mp/files/pages/files/wef1601-digitaltransformation-1401.pdf

11 World Economic Forum White Paper, in collaboration with Accenture, "Digital Transformation of Industries – Demystifying Digital and Securing $100 Trillion for Society and Industry by 2025," January 2016. http://reports.weforum.org/digital-transformation/wp-content/blogs.dir/94/mp/files/pages/files/wef1601-digitaltransformation-1401.pdf

12 World Economic Forum White Paper, in collaboration with Accenture, "Digital Transformation of Industries – Demystifying Digital and Securing $100 Trillion for Society and Industry by 2025," January 2016. http://reports.weforum.org/digital-transformation/wp-content/blogs.dir/94/mp/files/pages/files/wef1601-digitaltransformation-1401.pdf

13 World Economic Forum White Paper, in collaboration with Accenture, "Digital Transformation of Industries – Demystifying Digital and Securing $100 Trillion for Society and Industry by 2025," January 2016. http://reports.weforum.org/digital-transformation/wp-content/blogs.dir/94/mp/files/pages/files/wef1601-digitaltransformation-1401.pdf

14 © Accenture

15 Accenture Research

16 Accenture Research

17 © Accenture

18 Accenture Research

19 Accenture Research

20 Accenture Research

21 Accenture Research

22 Accenture Research

23 Accenture Research

24 © Accenture

25 © Accenture

26 Accenture Research

27 © Accenture

28 © Accenture

Chapter 4

1 © Accenture

2 © Accenture

3 © Accenture

4 © Accenture

5 © Accenture

6 http://www.swp.de/heidenheim/lokales/giengen/bsh-will-kuehlschraenke-per-smartphone-steuern-7763920.html, accessed January 24, 2017

7 World Economic Forum, in collaboration with Accenture, "Digital Transformation of Industries: Automotive Industry," January 2016. https://www.accenture.com/t20160505T044104__w__/us-en/_acnmedia/PDF-16/Accenture-wef-Dti-Automotive-2016.pdf

8 Accenture, "Analytics – Insight-Driven Growth in Automotive and Industrial Equipment," 2015. https://www.accenture.com/t00010101T000000__w__/gb-en/_acnmedia/PDF-4/Accenture-AIE-Analytics-Brochure-Final.pdf

9 https://datasundae.com/category/iot/, accessed December 8, 2016

10 © Accenture

Chapter 5

1 IDC, "IDC FutureScape: Worldwide CIO Agenda 2016 Predictions," November 2015

2 © Accenture, based on: IDC, "IDC FutureScape: Worldwide IT Industry 2016 Predictions – Leading Digital Transformation to Scale," November 2015; https://hbr.org/2016/02/companies-are-reimagining-business-processes-with-algorithms, accessed January 26, 2017; IDC, "IDC Accelerating Innovation on the 3rd Platform," March 2015; IDC, "IDC FutureScape: Worldwide CIO Agenda 2016 Predictions," November 2015; http://www.informationweek.com/healthcare/3d-printingbreakthrough-could-change-healthcare/d/d-id/1322856, accessed January 26, 2017; IDC, "IDC FutureScape: Worldwide Datacenter 2016 Predictions," November 2015

3 © Accenture

4 http://www-01.ibm.com/common/ssi/cgi-bin/ssialias?infotype=PM&subtype=AB&htmlfid=IMC14702USEN, accessed January 20, 2017

5 © Accenture

6 http://www.zf.com/corporate/en_de/products/product_range/commercial_vehicles/zukunftsfaehigkeit/fit_for_the_future.html, accessed January 24, 2017

7 http://www-03.ibm.com/software/businesscasestudies/hr/hr/corp?synkey=M-200424F25312E29, accessed January 24, 2017

8 © Accenture

9 © Accenture

10 © Accenture

Chapter 6

1 © Accenture

2 Accenture Research

3 http://www.pcadvisor.co.uk/feature/broadband/5g-release-date-3632607/, accessed January 24, 2017
4 © Accenture
5 Gartner, "Predicts 2014: Manufacturer R&D Gets Smarter About Innovation in the Digitalized Era," December 2013
6 http://www.aerospacemanufacturinganddesign.com/article/millions-of-data-points-flying-part2-121914/, accessed February 1, 2017
7 http://www.datasciencecentral.com/profiles/blogs/that-s-data-science-airbus-puts-10-000-sensors-in-every-single, accessed January 15, 2017
8 http://www.forbes.com/sites/gilpress/2015/11/10/transform-or-die-idcs-top-technology-predictions-for-2016/#4fe6e4827cec, accessed January 24, 2017
9 © Accenture
10 http://www.stratasys.com/resources/case-studies/aerospace/aerialtronics, accessed January 25, 2017
11 http://www.javelin-tech.com/3d-printer/ducati-accelerates-engine-design-with-fdm-prototyping/, accessed January 25, 2017
12 http://www.stratasys.com/resources/case-studies/automotive/bmw, accessed January 25, 2017
13 http://www.stratasys.com/resources/case-studies/automotive/honda-access?returnUrl=http://www.stratasys.com/resources/case-studies?industries=Automotive, accessed January 25, 2017
14 http://www.gereports.com/post/77131235083/jet-engine-bracket-from-indonesia-wins-3d-printing/, accessed January 25, 2017
15 © Accenture
16 © Accenture
17 https://www.tesla.com/support/software-updates, accessed January 27, 2017
18 http://knowledge.insead.edu/customers/to-succeed-at-crowdsourcing-forget-the-crowd-4227, accessed January 25, 2017
19 http://en.dcnsgroup.com/parole-expert/virtual-reality-and-augmented-reality-their-naval-defence-applications/, accessed January 25, 2017
20 © Accenture
21 Accenture Research

Chapter 7

1 © Accenture
2 Accenture Research
3 © Accenture

4 Accenture Research

5 http://articles.sae.org/14207/, accessed February 16, 2017

6 Accenture, "Machine Dreams – Making the most of the Connected Industrial Workforce," 2016. https://www.accenture.com/t20160506T052209__w__/us-en/_acnmedia/PDF-13/Accenture-Connected-Industrial-Workforce-Research.pdf#zoom=50

7 © Accenture

8 Accenture, "Machine Dreams – Making the most of the Connected Industrial Workforce," 2016. https://www.accenture.com/t20160506T052209__w__/us-en/_acnmedia/PDF-13/Accenture-Connected-Industrial-Workforce-Research.pdf#zoom=50

9 Accenture, "Machine Dreams – Making the most of the Connected Industrial Workforce," 2016. https://www.accenture.com/t20160506T052209__w__/us-en/_acnmedia/PDF-13/Accenture-Connected-Industrial-Workforce-Research.pdf#zoom=50

10 Accenture, "Machine Dreams – Making the most of the Connected Industrial Workforce," 2016. https://www.accenture.com/t20160506T052209__w__/us-en/_acnmedia/PDF-13/Accenture-Connected-Industrial-Workforce-Research.pdf#zoom=50

11 Pollock, Sara, "Final Destination: Organizational Transparency," Clear Company Blog, April 3, 2014. http://blog.clearcompany.com/final-destination-organizational-transparency

12 Accenture, "Machine Dreams - Making the most of the Connected Industrial Workforce," 2016. https://www.accenture.com/t20160506T052209__w__/us-en/_acnmedia/PDF-13/Accenture-Connected-Industrial-Workforce-Research.pdf#zoom=50

13 © Accenture

14 World Economic Forum, in collaboration with Accenture: "Digital Transformation of Industries: Digital Enterprise," January 2016. http://reports.weforum.org/digital-transformation/wp-content/blogs.dir/94/mp/files/pages/files/digital-enterprise-narrative-final-january-2016.pdf

15 © Accenture

16 Accenture, "Judgment calls – Preparing leaders to thrive in the age of intelligent machines," 2016. https://www.accenture.com/t20161221T043743__w__/us-en/_acnmedia/PDF-12/Accenture-Strategy-Workforce-Judgment-Calls.pdf

17 World Economic Form, "The Future of Jobs - Employment, Skills and Workforce Strategy for the Fourth Industrial Revolution," January 2016. http://www3.weforum.org/docs/WEF_Future_of_Jobs.pdf

18 © Accenture, based on "The Future of Employment: How Susceptible are Jobs to Computerization?," Frey, C. & Osborne, M. (2013)

19 World Economic Form, "The Future of Jobs - Employment, Skills and Workforce Strategy for the Fourth Industrial Revolution," January 2016. http://www3.weforum.org/docs/WEF_Future_of_Jobs.pdf

Chapter 8

1 Accenture, "Incubator or Respirator? – Why you need to change the way you innovate. Now.," 2015. https://www.accenture.com/t20160629T222744__w__/us-en/_acnmedia/Accenture/Conversion-Assets/DotCom/Documents/Global/PDF/Strategy_7/Accenture-Strategy-Incubator-or-Respirator-Change-the-Way-You-Innovate.pdf

2 Accenture, "Incubator or Respirator? – Why you need to change the way you innovate. Now.," 2015. https://www.accenture.com/t20160629T222744__w__/us-en/_acnmedia/Accenture/Conversion-Assets/DotCom/Documents/Global/PDF/Strategy_7/Accenture-Strategy-Incubator-or-Respirator-Change-the-Way-You-Innovate.pdf

3 http://www.pcworld.com/article/155984/worst_tech_predictions.html, accessed December 8, 2016

4 http://www.pcworld.com/article/155984/worst_tech_predictions.html, accessed December 8, 2016

5 Accenture, "Beyond the Product: Rewriting the Innovation Playbook," 2016. https://www.accenture.com/t20160907T071628__w__/us-en/_acnmedia/PDF-17/Accenture-Innovation-Driven-Growth-Umbrella-PoV-1.pdf#zoom=50

6 © Accenture, based on: World Economic Forum, in collaboration with Accenture, "Digital Transformation of Industries: Digital Consumption," January 2016. https://www.accenture.com/t20160503T050949__w__/hu-en/_acnmedia/PDF-16/Accenture-Digital-Consumption.pdf; Accenture, "Thriving on disruption," 2015. https://www.accenture.com/t20160215T053953__ w__/us-en/_acnmedia/Accenture/Conversion-Assets/Outlook/Documents/1/Accenture-Thriving-On-Disruption-Web-PDF.pdf#zoom=50; Accenture, "Mastering operational flexibility," 2016. https://www.accenture.com/t20160628T022829__w__/us-en/_acnmedia/PDF-24/Accenture-Mastering- Operational-Flexibility-POV.pdf; http://www.mckinsey.com/business-functions/strategy-and-corporate-finance/our-insights/strategic-principles- for-competing-in-the-digital-age, accessed January 30, 2017; http://www.stratasys.com/resources/case-studies/automotive/honda-access, accessed January 30, 2017

7 © Accenture

8 © Accenture

9 http://www.ceasiamag.com/2016/03/bosch-launches-cloud-connected-world-iot-conference-berlin/, accessed January 26, 2017

10 http://www.expressbpd.com/healthcare/trade-trends/carestream-wins-2016-north-america-frost-and-sullivan-award-for-new-product-innovation-leadership/221260/, accessed January 26, 2017

11 https://www.bloomberg.com/news/articles/2016-01-04/intel-buys-ascending-technologies-in-further-drone-push, accessed January 26, 2017

12 © Accenture

13 © Accenture

14 © Accenture

15 © Accenture

16 © Accenture, based on: https://www.merkleinc.com/blog/transforming-consumer-behavior-through-mobile-data-science, accessed January 30, 2017; http://www.caterpillar.com/en/news/corporate-press-releases/h/caterpillar-and-uptake-to-create-analytics-solutions.html, accessed January 30, 2017; World Economic Forum, in collaboration with Accenture, "Industrial Internet of Things: Unleashing the Potential of Connected Products and Services," January 2015. http://www3.weforum.org/docs/WEFUSA_IndustrialInternet_Report2015.pdf; https://www.theguardian.com/media/2014/feb/23/netflix-viewer-data-house-of-cards, accessed January 27, 2017; http://www.businesswire.com/news/home/20160331005382/en/Pitney-Bowes-Launches-Single-Customer-View-Software, accessed January 30, 2017; http://www.mckinsey.com/global-themes/asia-pacific/a-ceos-guide-to-innovation-in-china, accessed January 30, 2017; http://blogs.wsj.com/cio/2015/ 05/04/apple-healthkit-helps-cedars-sinai-tackle-patient-engagement-challenge/, accessed January 30, 2017; https://consumergoods.com/2016-review-outlook-innovation-trends, accessed January 30, 2017

17 © Accenture

18 Accenture, "Incubator or Respirator? – Why you need to change the way you innovate. Now.," 2015. https://www.accenture.com/t20160629T222744__w__/us-en/_acnmedia/Accenture/Conversion-Assets/DotCom/Documents/Global/PDF/Strategy_7/Accenture-Strategy-Incubator-or-Respirator-Change-the-Way-You-Innovate.pdf

19 https://business.lesechos.fr/directions-numeriques/digital/transformation-digitale/0211405096985-schneider-electric-doit-apprendre-a-s-adapter-301320.php, accessed January 26, 2017

Chapter 9

1 https://www.theguardian.com/technology/2014/oct/30/china-xiaomi-third-biggest-smartphone, accessed January 27, 2017

2 Accenture, "Bridgemakers: Guiding Enterprise Disruption through Open Innovation," 2015. https://www.accenture.com/t20150523T033707__w__/us-en/_acnmedia/Accenture/Conversion-Assets/DotCom/Documents/Global/PDF/Dualpub_9/Accenture-Bridgemakers-Guiding-Enterprise-Disruption.pdf#zoom=50

3 © Accenture

4 The Center for Global Enterprise, "The Rise of the Platform Enterprise," January 2016. http://www.thecge.net/wp-content/uploads/2016/01/PDF-WEB-Platform-Survey_01_12.pdf

5 http://www.billboard.com/biz/articles/news/1559622/seven-ways-itunes-changed-the-music-industry, accessed January 26, 2017

6 https://www.statista.com/statistics/276623/number-of-apps-available-in-leading-app-stores/, accessed January 26, 2017

7 http://www.go-globe.com/blog/alibaba-statistics-trends/, accessed January 25, 2017

8 http://www.handelsblatt.com/my/unternehmen/mittelstand/betonpumpenbauer-putzmeister-hochbetrieb-auf-der-virtuellen-baustelle/14896760.html?ticket=ST-2296993-eXA6aYU47vxc9bUNbOb3-ap2, accessed January 26, 2017

9 acatech, "Smart Service Welt – Recommendations for the Strategic Initiative Web-based Services for Businesses," March 2014. http://www.acatech.de/fileadmin/user_upload/Baumstruktur_nach_Website/Acatech/root/de/Projekte/Laufende_Projekte/Smart_Service_Welt/BerichtSmartService_engl.pdf

10 © Accenture

11 © Accenture, based on The Center for Global Enterprise, "The Rise of the Platform Enterprise," January 2016. http://www.thecge.net/wp-content/uploads/2016/01/PDF-WEB-Platform-Survey_01_12.pdf

12 http://www.pcworld.com/article/2602260/mercedesbenz-maker-daimler-gets-deeper-into-ridesharing.html, accessed December 8, 2016

13 Accenture, "Five Ways to Win with Digital Platforms," 2016. https://www.accenture.com/lu-en/_acnmedia/PDF-29/Accenture-Five-Ways-To-Win-With-Digital-Platforms-Full-Report.pdf

14 Accenture, "Five Ways to Win with Digital Platforms," 2016. https://www.accenture.com/lu-en/_acnmedia/PDF-29/Accenture-Five-Ways-To-Win-With-Digital-Platforms-Full-Report.pdf

15 Accenture, "Five Ways to Win with Digital Platforms," 2016. https://www.accenture.com/lu-en/_acnmedia/PDF-29/Accenture-Five-Ways-To-Win-With-Digital-Platforms-Full-Report.pdf

16 Accenture, "Five Ways to Win with Digital Platforms," 2016. https://www.accenture.com/lu-en/_acnmedia/PDF-29/Accenture-Five-Ways-To-Win-With-Digital-Platforms-Full-Report.pdf

Chapter 10

1 http://archive.fortune.com/2007/05/01/magazines/fortune/kurzweil.fortune/index.htm, accessed January 25, 2017

2 http://support.hp.com/gb-en/document/c03760650, accessed January 26, 2017

3 http://www.rpdintl.com/, accessed January 26, 2017

4 http://www.cooperationcommons.com/node/416, accessed February 3, 2017

5 World Economic Forum, "Deep Shift - Technology Tipping Points and Societal Impact," September 2015. http://www3.weforum.org/docs/WEF_GAC15_Technological_Tipping_Points_report_2015.pdf

Index

About the Author

Eric Schaeffer is a Senior Managing Director at Accenture. He is leading Accenture's Digital Industry X.0 program with the objective of supporting industrial companies in harnessing digital opportunities – new services and business models – and transformation waves spanning across the whole enterprise.

Schaeffer also leads one of Accenture's global business services – Accenture Product Lifecycle Services – which provides end-to-end services to unlock value and efficiencies from product data across the engineering value chain, from the innovation and product development through to the manufacturing, aftersales and warranty services.

Schaeffer's primary industry focus is automotive and industrial equipment manufacturers, his secondary industry focus is freight and logistics and transportation and travel. His project track record covers business transformation programs encompassing complex business and technology changes and he has lead such programs for large and multinational companies.

Prior to his current global Industrial role at Accenture, Schaeffer was responsible for Accenture's Products (Industrial, Consumer Goods, Pharma and Retail) practice in France, Germany and Switzerland.

Schaeffer joined Accenture in 1987. His background is in Engineering and he studied at *École Supérieure d' Electricité*.

He is based in Paris, France.